UNSTUCK

FRESH TRACTION FOR COMMON STRUGGLES

JAMES MACDONALD

LifeWay Press®
Nashville, Tennessee

Neil Wilson
Bible Study Developer

Joel Polk
Editorial Team Leader

Reid Patton
Content Editor

Brian Daniel
Manager, Short-Term Discipleship

David Haney
Production Editor

Michael Kelley
Director, Groups Ministry

Jon Rodda
Art Director

Published by LifeWay Press® • © 2018 James MacDonald

ISBN 978-1-5359-2247-0 • Item 005806752

Dewey decimal classification: 248.84
Subject headings: PROBLEM SOLVING / CHRISTIAN LIFE / PROVIDENCE AND GOVERNMENT OF GOD

Unless indicated otherwise, all Scripture quotations are taken from The Holy Bible, English Standard Version® (ESV®), copyright © 2001 by Crossway, a publishing ministry of Good News Publishers. Used by permission. Scriptures marked NIV are taken from the Holy Bible, New International Version®, NIV®. Copyright © 1973, 1978, 1984, 2011 by Biblica, Inc.™ Used by permission of Zondervan. All rights reserved worldwide. www.zondervan.com. The "NIV" and "New International Version" are trademarks registered in the United States Patent and Trademark Office by Biblica, Inc.™ Scripture quotations marked NKJV are taken from the New King James Version®. Copyright © 1982 by Thomas Nelson. Used by permission. All rights reserved.

To order additional copies of this resource, write to LifeWay Resources Customer Service; One LifeWay Plaza; Nashville, TN 37234; fax 615-251-5933; order online at LifeWay.com; phone toll free 800-458-2772; email orderentry@lifeway.com; or visit the LifeWay Christian Store serving you.

Printed in the United States of America

Groups Ministry Publishing • LifeWay Resources • One LifeWay Plaza • Nashville, TN 37234

CONTENTS

THE AUTHOR

JAMES MACDONALD (DMin, Phoenix Seminary) is the founder and senior pastor of Harvest Bible Chapel. Beginning in 1988 with eighteen people, Harvest now welcomes thirteen thousand people to its seven Chicago-area campuses each week. Dr. MacDonald's practical teaching of God's Word is also heard daily around the world on radio and TV through the program *Walk in the Word,* and more than 170 vertical churches have been planted on four continents under his leadership. Dr. MacDonald and his wife, Kathy, live in the suburbs of Chicago near their seven grandchildren and three adult children, who serve alongside them in ministry.

For more information about James and these ministries, visit harvestbiblechapel.org or walkintheword.org.

Other Books and Bible Studies by James MacDonald

Act Like Men Bible study (LifeWay, 2018)

Act Like Men (Moody, 2014)

Always True: God's Promises When Life Is Hard Bible study (LifeWay, 2011)

Always True: God's Five Promises for When Life Is Hard (Moody, 2011)

Authentic: Developing the Disciplines of a Sincere Faith Bible study (LifeWay, 2013)

Authentic (Moody, 2013)

Come Home Bible study (LifeWay, 2014)

Come Home (Moody, 2013)

Downpour: He Will Come to Us Like the Rain Bible study (LifeWay, 2006)

Gripped by the Greatness of God (Moody, 2005)

Lord, Change Me (Moody, 2012)

Lord, Change My Attitude Before It's Too Late Bible study (LifeWay, 2008)

Lord, Change My Attitude ... Before It's Too Late (Moody, 2001)

Seven Words to Change Your Family (Moody, 2001)

Ten Choices: A Proven Plan to Change Your Life Forever (Thomas Nelson, 2008)

Think Differently Bible study (LifeWay, 2016)

Vertical Church Bible study (LifeWay, 2012)

Vertical Church (David C Cook, 2012)

When Life Is Hard Bible study (LifeWay, 2010)

When Life Is Hard (Moody, 2010)

The Will of God IS the Word of God (B&H, 2017)

Visit LifeWay.com for information about James MacDonald Bible studies.

INTRODUCTION

Not long ago I traveled to Michigan to show a prospective employee around a camp owned by our church. After walking through the buildings, we both climbed into my four-wheel drive truck to tour the wooded, hilly, snowbound site. We hadn't done a lot of plowing, but I had plenty of power under the hood, so I was confident my vehicle could manage the snowy terrain.

Things got exciting when we drove down a narrow trail and came around a curve at the bottom of a little hill. I knew I had to increase my speed to get up the climb, so I jammed the accelerator. The engine roared, but we didn't make it. Just a few feet from the top, the wheels started spinning, and our forward progress stopped.

As we rolled back, the guy who was with me said, "Go at it harder." That was all the challenge I needed. I gave it more gas and went for it. The hill refused to be conquered. And this time as we retreated, the truck slipped off the trail into deep snow. The wheels spun, but we couldn't move. *Stuck* is the word that comes to mind. Sometimes, though, more important stuff than our vehicle gets stuck.

Welcome to this Bible study, *Unstuck: Fresh Traction for Common Struggles.* God has given us His Word to meet us where we are. When He finds us stuck, He wants to give us traction. I pray that over the next six weeks you'll discover God's ever-present help for people who are stuck, feel stuck, or have already gained traction and want others to know the biblical principles that set them free.

HOW TO GET THE MOST FROM THIS STUDY

1. Attend each group session.
   - → Watch the video teaching.
   - → Participate in the group discussions.

2. Complete the personal studies in this Bible study book.
   - → Read the daily lessons.
   - → Complete the learning activities.
   - → Memorize each week's suggested memory verse.
   - → Take an honest look at where you're stuck and follow the guidance of the Holy Spirit to find fresh traction.

WEEK 1

GETTING UNSTUCK FROM DEPRESSION

Welcome to group session 1.

Have members introduce themselves by name. When the introductions are over, open the floor for comments about funny or serious circumstances that people might describe as being stuck. Then use the following questions to prepare the group for the video teaching.

When is a time you've felt stuck? What did it take to get unstuck?

Depression, the topic of session 1, can refer to significant clinical cases. Let's look at the definition of *depression* we'll use in this week's study:

> *A temporary emotional state characterized by exaggerated, extended feelings of hopelessness that aren't consistent with reality*

Why is depression such a common struggle?

This Bible study is designed not only to help us deal with our own struggles but also to equip us to sense and respond with compassion to the struggles of others. Our life example for this week's discussion is Elijah, a prophet in the Old Testament.

Before we watch the video, let's read a New Testament summary of Elijah's life:

> *Confess your sins to one another and pray for one another, that you may be healed. The prayer of a righteous person has great power as it is working. Elijah was a man with a nature like ours, and he prayed fervently that it might not rain, and for three years and six months it did not rain on the earth. Then he prayed again, and heaven gave rain, and the earth bore its fruit.*
> **JAMES 5:16-18**

WATCH

Use this guide to follow along as you watch video session 1.

How Dark Are the Clouds?

1. Downcast: Things are bad right now.

2. Discouragement: Things have been bad for a while.

3. Depression: Everything is bad.

4. Despair: It will never be any different; nothing will change it.

Depression

A temporary emotional state characterized by exaggerated feelings of sadness and hopelessness that are not consistent with reality

Understanding the Timing of Depression

1. After intense ministry output

2. After relational conflict

3. After physical exhaustion

4. After a major victory

5. After a huge disappointment

How to Get Depressed

1. Find a place by yourself.

2. Focus on the negative.

3. Forget God's provision for you.

Choosing the Cure to Depression

1. Let God confront you.

2. Let God reveal Himself to you.

3. Receive God's provision for you.

4. Do what God says immediately.

5. Get involved with people again.

Video sessions available at lifeway.com/unstuck
or with a subscription to smallgroup.com

Discuss the video teaching with your group.

Pastor James defined *depression* as "a temporary emotional state characterized by exaggerated, extended feelings of sadness and hopelessness that aren't consistent with reality." How does this definition help you understand some of your experiences in life?

Elijah's experience in 1 Kings is a case study in the causes and timing of emotional depression. Pastor James isolated five different causes. What were they? What parallel examples can you give from observation or your own life?

Elijah made three poor choices in 1 Kings 19:3-10 that turned his feelings into wrong conclusions. What were they? How could he have chosen differently in each case?

Which one of the cures for depression mentioned in the video teaching struck you as most unexpected or hopeful? Why?

APPLICATION. We follow a Savior who was made like us in every way (see Heb. 2:17) and who was "acquainted with grief" (Isa. 53:3). When we're upset and depressed, we find comfort in the life, suffering, death, and resurrection of Jesus. Approaching Him, we find One who sympathizes with our sorrow. Pray that God will help us take our depression and hand it over to Jesus Christ as we seek to empathize with and help one another become unstuck from depression.

THIS WEEK'S MEMORY VERSE

> *God is our refuge and strength,*
> *a very present help in trouble.*
> **PSALM 46:1**

ASSIGNMENT. Complete this week's personal study before the next group session. Make notes of any questions you want to discuss with other group members. Pray for members of your group by name, asking the Holy Spirit to remind them of God's answers to depression.

SLIPPERY ROAD AHEAD

When someone sighs and says, "I'm depressed," what should our response be? Or when we find ourselves using that word to describe our feelings, what are we actually saying? Calling something depression doesn't make it so, but the term can refer to one stage in a downward emotional and sometimes physiological spiral that probably won't go away if we ignore it.

Certain experiences come before and after depression. The progression begins with being *downcast* (see Ps. 42:5), as in "I'm having a bad day." This is the kind of disappointing discovery we can make at any time, reminding us that life can take unexpected turns we hadn't planned. If we fail to use these clues to remind ourselves that we aren't in control but God is, our downcast condition may persist. Then *discouragement* can develop: "I'm having a bad week." When we don't handle the occasional stumble in a healthy way, a pattern starts to form. The focus shifts from what's happening to the way we're feeling about it. This is followed by *depression* and the sense that "I don't know what's wrong, and I can't seem to shake it." Unresolved depression can lead to *despair,* expressed in the statement "Everything's wrong, and it's never going to change."

Each of these stages is marked by increased hopelessness and is more and more difficult to reverse. Our Bible study this week will take us into the life of Elijah to see this downward pattern develop and the way God works to free us from getting stuck in the cycle of depression.

Keep in mind throughout your personal study this week that our focus is on the spiritual causes of depression. We're not trying to address or solve effects caused by conditions like chemical imbalances, thyroid malfunction, or Parkinson's disease. These and other medical issues can have severe emotional side effects. If you're struggling with a pattern of depression, don't hesitate to seek medical confirmation. Ruling out physiological explanations can often help focus your attention on your spiritual responses to depression and on the health of your relationship with God.

DAY 1

THE SOUND OF SPINNING WHEELS

Depending on where you live, you may or may not be familiar with the sound of spinning wheels in the snow or mud. The sinking feeling you get is sometimes just an emotion caused by the noise; at other times it's the actual reality of knowing your tires are digging more deeply into whatever has eliminated their traction. You have an almost instinctive reaction to press the accelerator, thinking maybe spinning faster will allow you to escape the rut. But anyone who's ever been stuck can tell you this method rarely works. The admission that you're stuck is an important first step in deciding what you'll do next: wave down a passing motorist, call AAA, or put your wife behind the wheel and try to physically push the vehicle. Proactivity is better and more effective than negativity in such a situation.

The kind of depression we're thinking about this week is the common down part of the ups and downs of life. What internal signals warn you that things aren't quite right and that you may be stuck in depression?

As you trace the flow of events in Elijah's life, you'll see how he got to a bad place. By seeing how he got there, you can develop some understanding of yourself and the people you love. You'll also learn that God never forgets how frail and inconsistent we are. He doesn't accomplish great things as He did through Elijah because His servant was a superhero but in spite of His servant's flaws. If God can work through huge failures, He can work through us.

Briefly describe the following consecutive significant events in Elijah's life from 1 Kings 17–19.
1 Kings 17:1
1 Kings 17:2-7
1 Kings 17:8-16
1 Kings 17:17-24
1 Kings 18:1-16
1 Kings 18:17-19
1 Kings 18:20-40

1 Kings 18:41-46
1 Kings 19:1-8
1 Kings 19:9-18
Look back over the list of Elijah's significant events and mark each one with an up or down arrow, depending on the way it seems to have affected the prophet.

God wasn't done with Elijah after the three chapters we reviewed. The prophet came back in and did some amazing things before he turned over his mantle to Elisha, his replacement. He's also mentioned several memorable times later in Scripture. When Jesus was transfigured before His disciples on the mountain in Matthew 17:1-13, Elijah and Moses showed up to talk with Him in that glorious setting. Moses represented the law, and Elijah represented the prophets. The presence of these spiritual giants honoring Jesus not only affirmed Jesus' unique position as the Son of God but also reflected the way the Jews of that day thought of these two figures from their history.

Later James mentioned Elijah in the context of confession and prayer:

Confess your sins to one another and pray for one another, that you may be healed. The prayer of a righteous person has great power as it is working. Elijah was a man with a nature like ours, and he prayed fervently that it might not rain, and for three years and six months it did not rain on the earth. Then he prayed again, and heaven gave rain, and the earth bore its fruit.
JAMES 5:16-18

James mentioned Elijah to illustrate the power of prayer. So why did he feel compelled also to mention Elijah's shared human nature? He had just affirmed the power in the prayer of a righteous person. But before he gave his example, he anticipated our reluctance either to see ourselves as righteous or to expect our prayers to be as effective as Elijah's were; therefore, he reminded us that Elijah was just like us. His experiences getting emotionally stuck didn't invalidate his prayer life or his service to God. Likewise, God is still willing to use us.

Whom in your life do you trust to exchange confessions of sin and to pray for one another?

When has the lack or presence of such a person affected your spiritual life and, in particular, your ability to weather depressing events along the way?

James 5 places the prayers of Elijah in the context of praying and confessing sins (see. v. 16). It's crucial to remember that we don't confess our sins to one another and pray for one another in order to be forgiven; we confess to one another and pray for one another to be assured of forgiveness. God does the forgiving, and we prayerfully affirm His forgiveness when we witness confession.

How can confessing sin to a trusted brother or sister help you become unstuck from a pattern of sin that leads to depression?

Elijah was faithful, yet he was also human. His prayers were powerful and carried out under God's commands. Yet he demonstrated his shared human nature with us. Nevertheless, God graciously intervened and gave us a great example of both what to do and what not to do in the ups and downs of life. That's the exact point Paul made in 1 Corinthians:

> These things happened to [Old Testament believers] as an example, but they were written down for our instruction, on whom the end of the ages has come. Therefore let anyone who thinks that he stands take heed lest he fall. No temptation has overtaken you that is not common to man. God is faithful, and he will not let you be tempted beyond your ability, but with the temptation he will also provide the way of escape, that you may be able to endure it.
> **1 CORINTHIANS 10:11-13**

Each day this week we'll meditate on this memory verse:

> God is our refuge and strength,
>   a very present help in trouble.
> **PSALM 46:1**

Record at least five ways you understand God to be your refuge in times of trouble. Then turn them into a grateful prayer to end today's lesson.

DAY 2
UPS AND DOWNS

Perhaps you've noticed that feelings of depression don't necessarily follow difficult events in your life. Sometimes good times lead to a sense of burnout. Conversely, disastrous experiences sometimes bring out the best in us, forcing us to solve problems, depend on others, and turn to God. Depressed feelings aren't always predictable; therefore, we need to recognize early-warning signals that remind us to counteract the direction our lives are taking.

The acrostic HALT can help us watch for situations that set us up for a downward cycle of depression. The four letters stand for *hungry, angry, lonely,* and *tired*. Any of these conditions or a combination of them should set off a warning sign in our lives. Elijah certainly could have used that tool.

> **Considering what you've already learned about Elijah's life, note one or more instances that fit each of these early-warning signals.**
> **Hungry:**
> **Angry:**
> **Lonely:**
> **Tired:**
>
> **Which of these signs are most likely to create a loss of traction in your life?**
>
> **Compare Elijah's statements in 1 Kings 18:22 and 19:10. How do the different settings and audiences change the meanings?**

Based on major events in Elijah's life, we can trace at least five major triggers that can lead to feelings of depression. For Elijah, some of these triggers were bigger than life, leading to a very public showdown between God and Baal. Others were hidden pitfalls when the prophet's life was threatened by a powerful person.

By thinking about these events, we can look for the same kinds of triggers and identify the same devastating results in our lives. Below are five circumstances that can often lead to an emotional or psychological letdown, along with examples from Elijah's experience. For each trigger we want to consider the internal effects the prophet might have felt and then draw parallels to our own lives. If necessary, use the listed passages to refresh your memory.

1. AFTER INTENSE MINISTRY OUTPUT (SEE 1 KINGS 18:21-39). Elijah defeated and then destroyed the prophets of Baal. He was outnumbered. Standing alone, he was completely exposed if God didn't come through. He let the prophets of Baal go first and then mocked them even though he hadn't yet demonstrated God's power. Then he doubled down by soaking the sacrifice with water.

> **What range of feelings might Elijah have experienced at that point?**
>
> **Because all followers of Jesus are called to service and ministry, what represents intense ministry output for you?**
>
> **How do ministry successes and failures affect your relationship with God?**

2. AFTER RELATIONAL CONFLICT (SEE 1 KINGS 18:40-42A). Elijah had seen God deliver fire, and he was confident that God would deliver water, so he guaranteed a shocked and offended King Ahab that rain was coming. The hostility between Elijah and Ahab had been going on for three years.

> **How has prolonged relational conflict been draining for you?**
>
> **What would happen if you included God in your strategy for handling these conflicts?**

3. AFTER EXTREME PHYSICAL EFFORT (SEE 1 KINGS 18:42B-46). Different activities burn energy in different ways. Not only did Elijah strain in prayer for rain, but he also ran more than twenty miles from Mount Carmel to Jezreel.

> **What does Elijah's posture tell us about what he might have been feeling (see v. 42)?**

In what ways do you monitor and manage your levels of physical well-being throughout the day? What are you doing to build physical endurance?

4. AFTER A MAJOR VICTORY OR ACHIEVEMENT (SEE 1 KINGS 19:1). Ahab blamed everything on Elijah. The game changer for Elijah didn't change anything for Ahab other than leaving him short four hundred prophets of Baal.

How did the king miss the point of the miracle on Mount Carmel, and how might that resistance have affected Elijah?

In what ways do you keep victories in perspective and acknowledge that euphoria has a limited shelf life?

5. AFTER A HUGE DISAPPOINTMENT (SEE 1 KINGS 19:2-3). Not only was the king unaffected by the miracle, but the queen also made it her personal mission to kill the prophet. From the mountaintop of Carmel and the joyful jog to Jezreel, Elijah was suddenly running for his life. He didn't see that coming!

How does the temporary high of a great success sometimes make you vulnerable to a counterattack?

As you consider these triggers in your own experiences, take a few minutes to pray for others in your group who may be struggling this week. Consider calling someone in the group and asking him or her to pray for you about an area this study is addressing in your life.

By looking closely at Elijah's life, we get to see God in action. He's the main player and the most powerful participant. That's why this week's memory verse has the potential to create lasting effects in us:

God is our refuge and strength,
a very present help in trouble.
PSALM 46:1

We ended yesterday's study by meditating on God as our refuge. Today let's focus on God as our strength.

What in Elijah's story lets us know that he may not have been looking to God as his refuge and strength?

DAY 3
EASY STEPS TO DEPRESSION

One lesson from Elijah's life is that the factors that trigger depression and our internal responses may not lie in our control. But what we do next does. The distance between delight and defeat, triumph and terror is measured in the space between verses 2 and 3 in 1 Kings 19.

Given everything God had just done through Elijah, what are some reasons that explain his reaction in verse 3?

What are some other internal responses we might have to the kind of threatening news Elijah received?

Read Psalm 56:3. A response like fear, flight, or fight might be instinctive, but how do we prevent our initial feelings from being the deciding vote on what we do?

We don't suddenly fall into being stuck in depression. Once fear set in, Elijah walked a fairly predictable path into the valley of despair. And there's little evidence that he was listening for God's direction during this journey. We take recognizable steps that lead us to a predictable place. These steps aren't sequential; we can start with any one of them and end up in the same place. All three steps involve decisions we make, which means each step into depression can be avoided. Each one also suggests an alternative decision that can bring health, relief, and traction to our lives.

Describe how Elijah took each of the following steps into depression. Then answer the questions.

1. FINDING A PLACE OF ISOLATION. Read 1 Kings 19:3-4.

What did Elijah do that increased his sense of isolation? How did isolating himself from others increase the weight of his problems?

In what ways are you tempted to seek isolation in response to a sudden lack of traction? Describe the results.

2. FOCUSING ON THE NEGATIVE. Read 1 Kings 19:4-5,10,13-14.

Why did Elijah's out-of-sync perspective make it harder to see God's tenderness?

3. FORGETTING GOD AND HIS PROVISION. Read 1 Kings 19:4,10,13-14.

How did his attitude cause Elijah to remain unimpressed with God's amazing care for his needs?

What parallels to these steps do you see in your life today?

1.

2.

3.

Each step toward being stuck can also remind us of a step that can give us traction. Let's think about each of those opportunities.

1. Instead of finding a place of isolation, we can choose to regularly connect in community. We need small-group interaction, worship in a larger body of believers, and individual relationships that are healthy and challenging. Struggling alone is often a choice. We can also choose to let others help us and pray for us. We have to choose the risk of transparency as more desirable than the cycle of stuck, tractionless living that isolation offers us. The decision to seek isolation is ultimately an effort to treat God as if He weren't there.

2. Instead of focusing on the negative, we can seek a second opinion in God's Word and God's character. This doesn't mean we refuse to call bad things bad or to

recognize when things are wrong. It does mean that we can see beyond the immediate circumstance and seek to look at situations from God's perspective.

3. Instead of forgetting God's provision for us, we can intentionally memorize promises God has made and remember His past faithfulness as a step toward a hopeful tomorrow rather than a hopeless future. Though Jeremiah's writings were filled with grief, mingled among the sorrow we can appreciate the lasting gift he gave us in verses like this one:

> The steadfast love of the LORD never ceases;
>   his mercies never come to an end;
> they are new every morning;
>   great is your faithfulness.
> "The LORD is my portion," says my soul,
>   "therefore I will hope in him."

LAMENTATIONS 3:22-24

Which step to depression do you take most often?

In light of the previous answer, which of the positive, depression-resisting choices do you need to make a more significant part of your life? How will you do that?

Spend a moment meditating on this week's memory verse:

> God is our refuge and strength,
>   a very present help in trouble.

PSALM 46:1

Today think about the phrase "a very present help." Examine each word and record a short paragraph explaining how you've discovered this truth in your relationship with God.

As you end today's lesson, pray for the leader of this study. Ask God to help him or her personally benefit by helping others learn to get unstuck.

DAY 4
THE GOD OF TRACTION, PART 1

The events recorded in 1 Kings 19:5-19 reveal the degree to which God was involved not only in the preceding major events but also in Elijah's personal life. God intervened in at least five ways, and we can count on His doing the same things in our lives. We'll take two days to consider ways these crucial principles affect our lives.

When we last saw Elijah, he was headed out alone from Beersheba into the deep wilderness (see vv. 3-4). He wasn't looking for God. He wasn't looking for a way forward or a way back. He was looking for a way out. After a day of wandering in the desert, he found a tree to sit under and then informed God he wanted to die. Having given up, Elijah fell asleep under the tree. It was the first smart move he'd made since he prayed for rain. He rested without realizing that was part of God's answer.

What instances can you recall from your life when God gave you the gift of rest? How did it affect your outlook?

God ignored Elijah's request to die and instead sent an angel with food. The angel woke Elijah and directed him to take a break from resting and eat. Then he slept some more. Later the angel awakened and fed Elijah again. That rest and nourishment fueled the prophet's forty-day trip to Horeb in the desert. That's when God showed up personally. It was time to bring Elijah back to full effectiveness.

Today let's examine three of the ways God steps into our lives with a cure for depression. For each one, think of an experience of your own that represents a similar intervention by God.

1. GOD CONFRONTS (SEE 1 KINGS 19:9,13). Elijah struggled to accept God's questions, but the Lord was persistent. Much as He did with Job, God didn't argue with His prophet or explain Himself. But He did correct one factual mistake on Elijah's part. Elijah was wrong to consider himself the last man of God standing; there were still seven thousand God counted as His. God's confrontations usually lead to further responsibility. He had more work for Elijah to do.

Why did God ask His question "What are you doing here, Elijah?" twice (vv. 9,13)?

Compare Elijah's two answers. What do they indicate about him?

In what ways were Elijah's answers right, and how were they wrong?

What has God confronted you about? Why was this necessary for you to gain traction out of depression?

2. GOD REVEALS HIMSELF (SEE 1 KINGS 19:10-14). Elijah was listening to his own self-pity, fear, and loneliness rather than responding to the amazing way God was revealing Himself to His prophet. Fire, water, and food from heaven hadn't brought the prophet to humility. Even when God shook the world, Elijah wrapped his cloak around himself and expressed his stubborn victimhood again. So God issued fresh marching orders and sent Elijah back into the fray.

When have you had trouble hearing from the Lord? Why do you think that happened? How does ongoing sorrow obscure God's voice?

3. GOD PROVIDES (SEE 1 KINGS 19:6-8). Instead of gratitude and hopefulness when God supplied him with food and rest, Elijah remained discontented. We run the danger of assuming that being thankful is a wasted effort. God knows what we need, and He can supply it. Because He's God, He doesn't need our gratitude.

Yet God insists that we be grateful. Why? Because gratitude affects something at our core and nurtures a right relationship with God. God doesn't need our thanks and isn't sad when we don't express gratitude; He's sad about what ingratitude does to our soul. Romans 1:21 points to our failure to honor or thank God as the core ingredient of our sinful rebellion against Him. God doesn't need our thanks, but He's not required to meet our needs either. He graciously does so from His love for us, not because we're so likable.

What items are on your personal list of God's faithful provision?

How could gratitude alleviate some of our depressed feelings?

Recount what God has provided and done specifically in your life in the past month.

List at least three ways God has helped you this week.

1.

2.

3.

Turn God's providence into a prayer of gratitude.

Spend a moment meditating on this week's memory verse:

God is our refuge and strength,
   a very present help in trouble.
PSALM 46:1

Today meditate on what it means for you to be "in trouble." Like Elijah, how have you discovered God's willingness to meet you when you're in that place?

As you end this day's lesson, ask God to point out to you any ways you could be more open to His confrontation and correction. God has the ability to lead you out of your burdensome feelings. Pause and listen for His voice. Receive His grace and direction.

DAY 5
THE GOD OF TRACTION, PART 2

It's easy for us to recognize God's firmness in dealing with Elijah and miss His grace. And yet there was a lot of grace in their interaction. God isn't a pampering God; He's a perfecting God. And His application of grace and truth is always sure-handed. He gave Elijah everything he needed to have, and He told Elijah everything he needed to hear.

One of our greatest challenges in dealing with depression in ourselves and others is that we tend to lack grace toward others and to mistake self-pity for grace toward ourselves. As we take a final look at God's dealings with Elijah, let's keep in mind how God intends to relate to us and how we can learn to help others when they're struggling with a loss of traction.

After God confronted His prophet, revealed Himself, and provided for his most basic needs, He then issued fresh orders for Elijah.

4. GOD DIRECTS (SEE 1 KINGS 19:15-17). Instead of arguing with Elijah, God pushed him into action, making clear that it was time to move on. The break was over, and important prophetic work needed to be done. Elijah would need to appoint God's chosen replacement for himself and to serve as a king maker for Hazael in Syria and Jehu in Israel.

> **What opportunities do you have to serve others and meaningfully use your time instead of remaining isolated and overwhelmed?**

5. GOD REFOCUSES (SEE 1 KINGS 19:18-19). The Lord had a specific plan and a specific relationship with Elisha in Elijah's future.

> **Who in your life is depressed and would benefit from your reliance on God as you reach out to help them?**

How can you rely on a close friend or family member to help you see what God is doing around you?

Who in your life is struggling? Whom could you pray for in hopes that the Lord will use you to encourage and bring that person back into healthy fellowship with God's family?

Studying the events in Elijah's life has revealed a man who operated at high ministry output. But before you envy his role, remember that ministering in a context of spiritual warfare makes a day of physical labor look like a walk in the park. Ministry is absolutely draining. Pouring yourself out for other people makes you spiritually vulnerable. And the more important the relationship is to you, the more significant the conflict and its side effects. As your energy is depleted, you're left exhausted. The result can be a temporary emotional state characterized by exaggerated feelings of sadness and hopelessness that aren't consistent with reality. In other words, you may become depressed.

As we see with Elijah, depression shuts out the resources we need most: people to love us, relationships to support us, and friends to give us a reality check. Sometimes we isolate ourselves when we're down, and that's not a good plan. In fact, in the prison system, the way to break down an inmate is to put him in an isolation cell. How often do we choose this option for ourselves?

Use the following questions to reflect on your personal health. Place a check mark beside each one that's currently true of you.

□ Do you have fewer personal friends than you did a year ago?
□ Does it make you angry when the phone rings for you?
□ Are you retreating to the bedroom or somewhere else to get away from family?
□ Are you avoiding your small group or avoiding joining one?
□ Do you try not to make eye contact with people at church? Have you stopped going to church altogether?

The more of these questions you checked, the more likely it is that you're struggling with the kind of depression and lack of traction we've examined this week. Don't ignore these symptoms.

Based on your response, what issues do you need to address in your life? What would be a good first step?

Often the thing you need most can be the thing you avoid most. But count on God to do for you what He did for Elijah. Review the actions He took to make a way for Elijah and use the prophet's experience as a guide for gaining traction in your own life. For example, Elijah was under a tree after a day's walk into the wilderness. Though he wanted to be alone, God didn't abandon him but sent a messenger to him.

The fact that God also fed and blessed Elijah provides a good model for ministry. When someone is hurting, move toward them without judgment or condemnation and find out what they need. Let them know that you can not only listen but also be a supportive presence. As you're able, meet the need or connect them with others who can. Share God's Word with them. The Lord may give them traction through your compassion.

Starting with this subject wasn't a random choice. Depression can affect and become an aftereffect of other experiences of being stuck that we'll look at in the weeks to come. Keep the insights from this week's study in mind as you seek traction in other areas. And may you discover over and over the truth of this week's memory verse:

> *God is our refuge and strength,*
>   *a very present help in trouble.*
> **PSALM 46:1**

WEEK 2
GETTING UNSTUCK IN YOUR MARRIAGE

Welcome to session 2 of Unstuck.

Welcome anyone attending for the first time. Ask members to share a significant idea or experience from the previous group session or from their personal study this week on getting unstuck from depression. Use some or all of the following questions to prepare the group for the video teaching.

Share pre-wedding stories. What can you remember about the time, place, and circumstances when you asked someone to marry you or you were asked to marry someone?

Almost all of us have experienced weddings, even if we didn't directly participate. What's one of the most memorable incidents, serious or humorous, that you've seen at a wedding?

What would you say is a significant difference between being engaged and being married?

Last week we talked about being stuck alone in depression; this week we'll look at the common struggle of being stuck with a partner in marriage. In our society the term *stuck* often refers to the feelings experienced in an unwanted or unwise marriage. That's not the meaning intended in this Bible study. We're assuming God brought you and your spouse together, and His intention is that no person or circumstance should tear you apart. In this context, being stuck means a couple isn't going forward spiritually, isn't growing emotionally, and isn't meeting each other's physical needs. Everything has ground to a halt, and you don't know how to get unstuck. It's time for some traction.

Use this guide to follow along as you watch video session 2.

How Can You Get Unstuck in Your Marriage?

1. Prioritize your marriage.

2. Acknowledge your sinful bent.

3. Rally when times are toughest.

4. Let go of offense.

5. Focused delight.

You Know You're Neglecting Your Wife

1. When you give one-word answers to heartfelt questions

2. When you hide your feelings, giving only the facts when forced

3. When you refuse to schedule one-on-one time

4. When you do things that hurt, but you're not sorry

5. When you don't bring her good news first

Words That Heal

1. A word of regret

2. A word of confession

3. A word of affection

4. A word of hope

5. A word of commitment

Four Bad Alternatives to Conflict Resolution

1. Attack

2. Retreat

3. Hide

4. Surrender

Video sessions available at lifeway.com/unstuck
or with a subscription to smallgroup.com

Discuss the video teaching with your group.

Based on the video teaching, what are some obvious warning signs of a stuck marriage?

Read Proverbs 13:10; 15:17; 18:22. Based on these verses, what would you expect to happen to a marriage that's consistently treated as a low priority?

Marriage always consists of two flawed partners; neither is ever perfect. It's always easier to see what our mate might be doing to harm our marriage than it is to see what we're doing, but according to Proverbs 12:4 and 27:8, what kinds of damage are often done by both partners?

Forgiveness is a decision to release someone from an obligation that was created when they offended you. What happens to a married couple that's unwilling to forgive? Why are they stuck? (See Proverbs 10:12; 19:11.)

According to Proverbs 5:15-23, what kinds of actions or attitudes prevent delight from growing in a marriage?

APPLICATION. Read Ephesians 5:22-33 together. Marriage isn't an end in and of itself; it displays the unique relationship between Christ and His church. Based on these verses, what responsibilities do men and women have in a marriage? Why do these relationships also apply to people who aren't married?

THIS WEEK'S MEMORY VERSE

A man shall leave his father and his mother and hold fast to his wife, and they shall become one flesh. And the man and his wife were both naked and were not ashamed.
GENESIS 2:24-25

ASSIGNMENT. Complete this week's personal study before the next group session. Make notes of any questions you want to discuss with other group members. Pray for each couple and individual represented in your small group. If you're part of a couple, you and your partner should consider completing the first two days of personal study alone; then work side by side to complete the remaining three lessons.

SLIPPERY ROAD AHEAD

This week's lessons, like the others in *Unstuck*, are based on the Bible because we believe "all Scripture is breathed out by God" (2 Tim. 3:16). Every verse in the Bible is there for God's purposes. He doesn't want it updated or improved. "The law of the LORD is perfect," Psalm 19:7 says. God's Word is exactly what it needs to be. When we open the Book of Proverbs, written by Solomon and inspired by the Holy Spirit, we don't find just helpful pointers on marriage. We find reliable, authoritative, divine guidelines for a relationship designed and sustained by God.

The Book of Proverbs is extremely practical. Included among its teachings are five principles to help you maintain traction in marriage. These relational truths are taught in multiple proverbs, so we'll look at them in groups. All of these principles share in common the ideas of choosing and working. Our culture promotes good marriage as the rare result of a love lottery, while the Bible promotes great marriage as the result of wise work and dependence on God. The effort of marriage includes the areas of priorities, participants, purpose, pardon, and pleasure. The failure to address any one of these areas will lead to a loss of traction in marriage. When several of these principles are ignored, before long your marriage relationship will feel stuck. So what you're about to study this week can keep you from slipping in your relationship, as well as help you recover after sliding into a ditch.

Marriage was an original gift God gave human beings in the form of a unique, two-become-one relationship. But if one or both of you don't have a personal relationship with God through Jesus Christ, the chances of getting seriously stuck are very high. God's provision for what a woman needs is a godly man, and God's provision for what a man needs is a godly woman. The process of godliness begins in your life when you realize you're a sinner and you respond in faith to Jesus Christ as the One who died on the cross for your sins. The Bible makes it clear that the forgiveness you long for and life lived the way it was originally designed can be found only by trusting Jesus Christ. Once you're right with God, together you and your spouse will be able to experience the power and wisdom He brings to a relationship. No matter what has you bogged down, God wants to help you get unstuck.

While this week is geared to married couples, we recognize that not all people are married. However, the Bible frequently uses marriage to illustrate God's relationship with His people. For that reason it's helpful for all believers to consider what the Bible teaches on this topic. Additionally, some who are single now may marry in the future. Working through a study like this will help prepare you for that time.

DAY 1
PRIORITIES IN ACTION

There's a difference between stated priorities and demonstrated priorities. Saying something is a priority or promising to make something a priority means little if our actions don't back up our words. The Book of Proverbs includes pithy wisdom that applies in a powerful way to marriage. The steps we'll explore can make traction possible for a stuck couple by challenging them to prioritize their relationship.

Read Proverbs 13:10. Although this verse doesn't specifically mention marriage, how does its comparison of the results of pride and the results of accepting guidance relate to marriage?

One of the early problems with a stuck marriage is the unwillingness by one or both partners to admit that a problem exists. The word *insolence* in Proverbs 13:10 can also be translated *pride* or *arrogance*. The blind assertion that things are OK when they're not creates confusion and conflict.

If one partner blindly asserts, "My marriage is fine! It's no worse than my brother's marriage," the other partner's words of concern are going to be seen as the problem. The strife caused by not being willing to agree and to admit there's a problem, even if you don't yet know what it is, can keep a couple from actually addressing the real problem and getting traction.

The foundational step in gaining traction in marriage is admitting you've lost it. "Houston, we have a problem!" If you can't say that, there's really no way forward. You don't have a good marriage because you want one, because you tell people you have one, or even because you could teach a class on how to have a good one. You have a good marriage because you work on your marriage. If you want to get unstuck, you have to prioritize your marriage.

Describe three concrete ways you could work on your marriage.

1.

2.

3.

Our culture feeds us a constant message that a good marriage results from the mysterious gift of romantic love, which motivates all action. The problem is that romantic love, though a reality, isn't stable, constant, or lasting. It can come and go; it can wane or grow. It's no wonder that such a large percentage of all marriages in our culture, based on this romantic ideal, fail. When the feelings fade, couples assume there's no hope for the relationship. In reality, marriages are sustained by the covenant commitment between the husband and the wife rather than feelings of romantic affection.

Stop and consider the wisdom of the traditional marriage vows. Do you remember what you said?

> *I, [groom/bride], take you [bride/groom], to be my [wife/husband], to have and to hold from this day forward, for better or for worse, for richer, for poorer, in sickness and in health, to love and to cherish, until death do us part. As God is my witness, I give my promise.*

Those words include at least twelve promises, and not a single one is a promise to feel. They're all promises to act. When you're stuck as a couple, the reason can almost always be found in a failure to keep one or more of the wedding promises.

Review the previous wedding vows and underline the ones you need to talk over with your spouse, emphasizing not what you expect from him or her but what you're willing to work on more intentionally yourself.

Read Proverbs 15:17; 18:22. The first proverb pictures two kinds of marriage relationships. Describe the differences between a love-saturated meal of herbs and a hate-saturated meal of steak.

What are some factors that keep people from regularly working on their marriage?

It's easy to get distracted by comparing our marriage with others and assuming they're either worse or better than ours. We may learn from other marriages, but we still need to make those lessons work in our own marriage. We have to take responsibility to nurture and grow the amazing relationship in which God has placed us to do His work in our lives.

Is there a particular marriage you admire? How can you apply in your own marriage a lesson you've learned by observing that marriage?

This week we'll explore the biblical basics of marriage. Although these foundational beliefs are under assault in our culture, a biblical view of marriage compels us to affirm that all attempts to erase role distinctions based on gender are evil. Efforts to eradicate the significance of the complementary differences between men and women at the very design level are equally not of God. And exegetical gymnastics determined to deny the explicit statements of the Bible are an affront to the infinite wisdom and creative genius of Almighty God, who created man and woman in His image (see Gen. 1:26-27). Man and woman are equal in His eyes but different in their roles. Any effort to thwart God's design for marriage is folly. Efforts to follow God's design, however, will be rewarded.

Meditate on this week's memory verse:

A man shall leave his father and his mother and hold fast to his wife, and they shall become one flesh. And the man and his wife were both naked and were not ashamed.
GENESIS 2:24-25

As you end today's lesson, ask God's Spirit to bring to mind a specific way you could prioritize your marriage in the next twenty-four hours.

DAY 2
THE UNAVOIDABLE FLAW

Two foundational biblical passages on marriage create the framework for living out the practical wisdom of the proverbs we're looking at this week. These passages fly directly in the face of much of what our culture says about marriage.

> **Read Ephesians 5:22-33 and 1 Peter 3:1-7. What stands out most to you in these two statements about marriage, in contrast to what our culture believes?**

Did you notice that Ephesians 5:31 quotes this week's memory verse? God's involvement with marriage as Creator and Designer goes all the way back to the beginning. After the first two chapters of Genesis point out the ideal design for men and women, chapter 3 makes it clear that the fall has deeply affected the way men and women relate to each other in marriage. We need a Savior, Jesus Christ, to deal with our sin and empower us to live faithfully in a fallen, cursed world. If we want our marriage to go forward, both partners have to admit our sinful bent. The more we ignore the reality of sinful inclinations, the more we'll find ourselves stuck in offended expectations, broken promises, and consequences of sin. The more we both rely on Christ every day, the more we'll navigate the slippery spots on the road of life.

> **Read Proverbs 12:4; 27:8. Each of these proverbs focuses on the way one partner can significantly damage the marriage. Record some examples of the wrong actions these proverbs suggest.**

Each of us brings the capacity for sin into the marriage relationship. When we think something might be wrong in our marriage, our tendency will be to assume our partner is creating the problem rather than beginning with ourselves. These proverbs, which highlight the temptation to stray on the husband's part and the temptation to shame on the wife's part, are both examples of our flawed nature. These are long-standing human problems.

Read Genesis 3:8-13. In this encounter with God, what did each participant do when confronted with his or her sin?

What had changed in Adam and Eve between the creation of marriage in Genesis 2:24-25 and their self-perception in Genesis 3:8-10?

Adam and Eve's guilt and shame have been passed down to us. Denying and ignoring sin creates chaos in our relationships. The process of getting unstuck in marriage always starts with the recognition that there's a problem, then moves to the question, *How have I contributed to the problem?*

Read 1 John 1:8-9. What action steps do these verses prescribe when we're convicted of sin by the Holy Spirit, our conscience, or our mate?

Self-centered, sinful habits damage a marriage, and I could give you plenty of hard-learned principles from my own life. For example, men, here's how you know you're neglecting your wife.

- You give one-word answers to heartfelt questions. "Fine" isn't a real answer in any universe.

- You hide your feelings, giving facts only when forced. Press past the inclination to limit responses and work at interaction.

- You refuse to schedule one-on-one time. Uninterrupted, attentive conversation is one of the most valuable gifts you can give to your wife.

- You do things that hurt, but you're not sorry. Eventually, these actions build resentment and bitterness.

- You don't bring her good news first. Nothing says she's not the most important person in your life like choosing to share good news with someone else.

If one or more of these practices describe you, don't be surprised if your marriage is stuck. It's time to take a different approach.

Owning our capacity for sin and error in our most important relationship requires humility. Admitting we might not see what we're doing wrong and asking our husband or wife to help us see it may be the beginning of traction. If we see something in our mate that needs to be pointed out, we express humility, and in all cases we must speak with gentleness.

Read Ephesians 4:1-3. What are some ways these specific examples of living apply to the marriage relationship? How will following this wisdom help you become unstuck?

Each characteristic in verses 2-3 is corporate. In other words, it requires other believers as the context for action. For example, you can't be patient alone; that requires a real someone you must practice patience with. Who fits that category more than your spouse? Marriage is a prime environment for walking in the manner Christ called you to walk.

Spend time in reflection evaluating your marriage. What's one way you're sinning against your spouse? What would repentance look like in this particular situation?

If you can't identify a specific area of sin, for what could you express gratitude to your spouse? When will you verbalize this to him or her?

Spend a moment meditating on this week's memory verse:

A man shall leave his father and his mother and hold fast to his wife, and they shall become one flesh. And the man and his wife were both naked and were not ashamed.
GENESIS 2:24-25

As you end today's lesson, ask God's Spirit to help you grow in transparency about your flawed nature and ways it affects your relationship with God and with your spouse.

DAY 3
MOTIVATION DURING HARD TIMES

Sometimes when we agree there's a problem, we discover that it isn't the fault of either mate. External factors can intrude to add confusion, pain, and loss of traction in the marriage. Take, for example, a case in which a spouse, through no fault of their own, suddenly loses their job. That crisis can either present opportunities for shared problem solving or send the relationship sliding into the ditch of blame, fear, and desperation.

Identify external circumstances that can cause us to get stuck in marriage. Think specifically about your marriage. List at least five.

1.

2.

3.

4.

5.

When times are tough in your marriage, that's the time to rally together with your spouse. Difficulty often drives a wedge between a couple. They get caught up with the crisis and neglect their relationship, and sometimes they don't recover. Kathy and I have often said to each other, "Thank the Lord that the difficult things in life have driven us to our knees and together, not apart."

When an unforeseen problem rears its ugly head in your home, at what point does prayer together become part of your response plan? Why?

One reason couples don't turn to the Lord in prayer when they face hard times is that they don't talk to God together during good times. Another reason is that when they aren't blaming each other, they're blaming God for the problem. God is never at fault when our marriage becomes stuck. Living in a fallen world means that hardship comes to everyone. But God is still there in the middle of it all, inviting us to acknowledge His presence and count on His help. He will help us get unstuck.

> **Read Romans 8:28; 1 Corinthians 10:13; and James 1:3-5. Then respond to the prayer plan below by identifying at least three biblical perceptions of God's role when you face hardship.**
>
> **"Lord, when we as a couple face hard times, based on these promises from Your Word, we'll choose to believe You're doing the following for us even when we can't immediately see them."**
>
> 1.
>
> 2.
>
> 3.
>
> **Read Proverbs 17:17. How would you like to see your mate serve as a friend and sibling to you when you face hardship?**
>
> **Read Proverbs 25:11. After each example that follows, identify a current or potential difficulty in which you could speak life-giving words.**

A WORD OF REGRET. When hardship comes through no one's fault, our mate still needs to be assured we don't blame him or her. Saying, "I feel bad that this happened to us" is very different from "I feel bad that you caused this."

> **In what ways does your mate need assurance?**

A WORD OF HOPE. Verbalizing our confidence in God and praying with and for our mate during troubles bring life to our situation.

> **In what ways are you facing hopelessness?**

A WORD OF AFFECTION. We offer life-giving words to our mate when we assure them of our ongoing commitment and appreciation, especially when circumstances feel out of control. "I love you," "Thank you," and compliments are important all the time but are especially significant during crises.

How many words of affection has your mate received today?

Much of what we've considered today involves searching the Bible for wisdom and putting it into practice to help us get unstuck. Following biblical wisdom will lead us into joy, but we must also acknowledge that we need God's help to become truly unstuck. For this to happen, our marriages must reflect the gospel.

Marriage is designed to mirror Christ's relationship with the church. What can we learn from that model that we can apply to our marriage?

How would applying that wisdom help us get unstuck?

The fullest purpose of marriage is seen in Christ's relationship with the church. Getting unstuck happens when we reflect this gospel-rich relationship in our marriage.

Spend a moment meditating on this week's memory verse:

A man shall leave his father and his mother and hold fast to his wife, and they shall become one flesh. And the man and his wife were both naked and were not ashamed.
GENESIS 2:24-25

"One flesh" (v. 24) is more than a recognition of the sexual aspects of marriage. It speaks to oneness at every level—physical, emotional, mental, and spiritual. These areas continually need attention in a healthy, growing marriage.

As you end today's lesson, call or approach your mate and ask to pray for him or her. Simply thank the Lord for allowing you to spend your life with that person, facing together whatever lies ahead with His help.

DAY 4
THE RUT OF UNFORGIVENESS

Everything you know about forgiveness will be tested by marriage. There are no lasting relationships without forgiveness. Contrast this truth with a memorable movie line from the twentieth century, which expresses a worldly misunderstanding of this lifelong relationship: "Love means never having to say you're sorry."

The main reason that concept is a lie is that it overlooks the truth we confronted earlier this week about our own sin. In human relationships, each day presents a new reason to admit guilt and take responsibility. A biblical rewrite of that movie line would be "Love means being willing to say you're sorry and actually meaning it."

In marriage a lack of forgiveness builds up over time to rob the relationship of traction. Big offenses seldom cause marital loss of traction; it's the accumulation of little wrongs that haven't been addressed.

> **Read Proverbs 19:11. Describe and give examples of the two action phrases in this proverb.**
>
> **"Slow to anger":**
>
> **"Overlook an offense":**
>
> **Which of the following is closest to the truth? Explain your choice.**
> ☐ **Overlooking an offense means not even recognizing offenses or offenders.**
> ☐ **Overlooking an offense means being willing to forgive.**
> ☐ **Overlooking an offense means forgiving before being apologized to or even if not being asked to forgive at all.**

If you're not sure how offenses are handled in your marriage, here are four alternative responses we often substitute for forgiveness that have devastating effects in a relationship. If you recognize that one or more of these are your pattern, it's time to make forgiveness the default response. When an offense occurs, do you—

1. go on the attack, escalating the offense with more hurt?

2. retreat, escaping into silence and nursing the hurt?

3. hide, escaping into activities and work to avoid the conflict?

4. give up, adding another offense to your list of hopelessness?

Each of these responses not only avoids forgiveness but also destroys the priority of marriage, denies the reality of your mutual flawed tendencies, diminishes your capacity to overcome difficulties, and detracts from the possibility of delight in your spouse. Forgiveness, on the other hand, is key to gaining traction when the road of life turns slippery.

> **Review the four typical reactions to offenses that can become patterns in marriage. Which one(s) can you most relate to?**

Are you ready for the forgiving alternative?

> **Read Colossians 3:12-13. What standard and measurement does Paul specify for the kind of forgiveness a follower of Christ should offer?**

Forgiveness is releasing someone from the obligation that occurred when that person hurt you. For Christians, first, forgiveness is obedience to God. Second, forgiveness bears witness to the gospel that's at work in our hearts. We forgive because we've been forgiven. As Jesus forgives us, we forgive others—and forgiveness should begin inside our family.

> **Read Proverbs 10:12. In the words of this Proverb, why is covering all offenses with forgiveness better than trying to cover up those offenses?**

> **In your experience, what happens when you try to ignore or cover up offenses rather than forgive them?**

Let's briefly look at the other side of the equation. If we love someone and we know we've hurt them, we make it easier for them to forgive us by asking for it. This involves a confession of our wrongdoing and a request for pardon. Here are a few *wrong* ways to apologize.

- "I'm sorry." This is the most frequent and incomplete attempt at an apology. "I'm sorry" by itself basically says, "I care about how I feel, not necessarily about how you feel."

- "If I hurt you, I'm sorry." This isn't an apology. It's a rationalization followed by information. It means "I'm not taking responsibility for the pain I caused, and even if it could be proved that it was my fault, the best you're getting from me is a vague bad feeling."

- "I'm sorry I hurt you, but that wasn't my intent." Apology? No! It compounds the pain by minimizing our responsibility for the hurt we've caused.

- Here's the worst one: "Hey, I'm sorry you got hurt," which, translated, means "I'm sorry you're so sensitive and weak that my minor offense hurt you. It's really your own fault that it bothered you!"

Only one apology reflects a repentant heart that God will use to revitalize a relationship that needs healing: "I'm sorry. It's my fault. I was wrong when I hurt you. I have no excuse. Will you please forgive me?"

Why is this final form of apology hard for us to deliver?

An important part of the process is actually asking the person we hurt to forgive us and waiting for their response. Because we fear they may say no, we're often reluctant to be vulnerable and confess. But if we're unwilling to be vulnerable, how badly do we really want to be forgiven?

Ask God to show you any areas of unforgiveness you're holding against your spouse or others. Sit quietly long enough for Him to answer your prayer. If He brings any matters to mind, deliberately release them.

Spend a moment meditating on this week's memory verse. Consider ways a willingness to forgive your spouse is both a way to hold fast to each other and to maintain unity.

A man shall leave his father and his mother and hold fast to his wife, and they shall become one flesh. And the man and his wife were both naked and were not ashamed.
GENESIS 2:24-25

DAY 5
REFOCUSED DELIGHT

The final and crucial principle for keeping a marriage unstuck involves focused delight in the other person. That's how you originally got together. You had a world of people to choose from, but you picked him or her. Something about the way he or she talked, looked, acted, and thought attracted you. Each of you found what you wanted. Delight was the natural by-product of your newly formed relationship. As a result, working on your marriage was effortless.

> **Why are relationships easier at the beginning? What holds your interest in the initial phase of getting to know someone?**

> **How does the term *delight* apply to your marriage now in relation to all levels of intimacy?**

Once we're married, we often gravitate to selfishness and ingratitude. We harvest the benefits of a mate's strengths and then become focused on their shortcomings. We want to blame what's missing in our lives on the deficiencies of anyone but the person in the mirror. So we begin to punish the person closest to us because they didn't come through and make our lives what we wanted them to be. Gradually, a relationship that once had life becomes apparently lifeless, just as a vehicle in motion loses traction and slips sideways into a ditch.

The world looks at a relationship in that condition and says, "Haul that thing to the junkyard and get yourself a new model." God looks at a relationship in a rut and says, "I can make that just like new—and even better."

> **Read Proverbs 5:15-23. What kinds of actions or attitudes prevent delight from growing in a marriage?**

In a healthy, tracking marriage, two people delight in each other. You may have romantically slipped into marriage, but choosing to delight in your mate maintains and strengthens your relationship. The passage from Proverbs 5 includes clear sexual implications. The Bible frequently talks about sexuality, but it cloaks the intimate, personal, private portions of a man and woman's relationship with modesty. It preserves dignity, discovery, and delight by avoiding crude explicitness. The proverbs are written that way because they're describing what's beautiful and honorable in marriage. Four words capture aspects of a healthy sexual delight in marriage without removing the mystery.

1. **SINGULARITY.** If you're privileged to be married, your needs are to be met by one person.

2. **EXCLUSIVITY.** You share and preserve experiences that are between the two of you and no one else.

3. **FERVENCY.** You're increasingly engaged with each other in every part of your relationship.

4. **FREQUENCY.** You don't allow any aspect of your expressed delight in each other to slip away (see 1 Cor. 7:5).

Which one(s) of these four points of delight have had the strongest impact on your marriage? Which one(s) need attention?

If you could ask your spouse only one question about intimacy in your marriage, what would it be? Why haven't you asked the question?

As a couple, read aloud Ephesians 5:22-33 and 1 Peter 3:1-7.

Then take time on your own to list three ways you've seen your mate live up to the principles mentioned in these passages. Take turns sharing them with each other one at a time.

Complete this sentence and then share it with your wife or husband: It would bring me delight if we could more consistently ...

The teachings on marriage from the Book of Proverbs and other passages in the Bible should produce interesting conversations in your marriage. Husbands completing this study are charged with taking the lead and not losing the opportunities introduced in these lessons. Don't try to start everywhere, but start somewhere. Have a conversation. Ask your wife, "If we could work on one topic during this study, which one would you choose?" Make sure you've chosen at least one you want to work on as well.

For your final meditation on this week's memory verse, identify how many different examples of potentially delightful moments you can find in the verses.

A man shall leave his father and his mother and hold fast to his wife, and they shall become one flesh. And the man and his wife were both naked and were not ashamed.
GENESIS 2:24-25

The next two weeks of study will deal with a significant danger we've only introduced in this one. Much of the positive traction we've considered may be damaged or destroyed if past or ongoing sexual sin is present in our lives. These matters don't go away on their own. God has a lot to tell us that's both painful and hopeful. Weeks 1–2 have given us a good foundation to build on, and the Lord is going to give us plenty more help in getting unstuck in other areas of life.

WEEK 3
GETTING UNSTUCK FROM SEXUAL SIN: THE CRISIS

Welcome to session 3 of Unstuck.

After welcoming any newcomers to the group, take a moment to pray for this session. Thank God for the lessons from His Word over the past two weeks. Ask the Holy Spirit to open minds and hearts to what He wants each person to learn during your time together.

Use some or all of the following questions to prepare the group for the video teaching.

What significant discoveries or challenges from the past two weeks can you share with us as you've worked on the personal study as individuals or couples?

What role does change play in getting unstuck or gaining fresh traction for common problems?

What's a good example from your childhood of the possibility of change in a person's life?

In this session we'll discover not only that change is very much a part of life but also that real transformation follows a certain pattern. We don't improve randomly, but we can and do change. And understanding the possibility and pattern for such change becomes crucial when we face major issues in life that may appear unchangeable.

WATCH

Use this guide to follow along as you watch video session 3.

Overcoming Sexual Sin

1. I must admit that sexual sin is breaking God's law.

2. I must acknowledge the consequences of sexual sin.

3. I must repent of sexual sin.

4. I must renounce all rationalizations for sexual sin.

5. I must make restitution for sexual sin.

When I Break God's Law

1. God is not mocked.

2. Exposure is certain.

3. The consequences are going to be exponential.

4. Delay makes it worse.

5. Forgiveness doesn't erase consequences.

What Is Lost in Sexual Sin

1. Loss of mission

2. Loss of loyalty and integrity

3. Loss of common sense

4. Loss of fear

5. Loss of God's favor

Rationalizations for Sexual Sin

1. I deserve this (pleasure).

2. This is my only weakness (personal).

3. I can handle this (pride).

4. No one will ever know (private).

5. You'd have to know my situation (pity).

Video sessions available at lifeway.com/unstuck
or with a subscription to smallgroup.com

Discuss the video teaching with your group.

What's an area of your life in which you've changed, and how did the transformation come about?

Describe the difference between the crisis part and the process part of change. Why is each of those stages necessary to bring about lasting transformation?

What was your response to the statistics on sexual saturation that Pastor James mentioned in his opening remarks? What do you think would cause a societal crisis about our deteriorating morality?

If sexuality is meant to be expressed in marriage and marriage is meant to illustrate the gospel, why is sexual immorality particularly offensive to God?

In what ways are Corinthians 6:9-10 and Ephesians 5:3-5 crisis-producing passages? What's the crucial point to remember when we discover our sins in those lists?

Pastor James described the path to overcoming sexual sin. What steps are required? What would they look like in someone's life?

APPLICATION. Repentance may begin in the private chamber of your heart, but it can't stay there. Confession to someone you trust solidifies the impact of repentance. Because so much of sexual sin is often rationalized under the cover of privacy, breaking its power requires confession. To whom can you express your repentance, knowing they'll graciously keep you accountable? When will you take this step?

THIS WEEK'S MEMORY VERSE

Flee from sexual immorality. Every other sin a person commits is outside the body, but the sexually immoral person sins against his own body.
1 CORINTHIANS 6:18

ASSIGNMENT. Complete this week's personal study before the next group session. Make notes of any questions you want to discuss with other group members. Pray for each member of your group by name, asking the Holy Spirit to help them recognize and respond to any crisis related to sexual sin in their lives.

SLIPPERY ROAD AHEAD

All change consists of a crisis and a process. Both are needed. But some spiritual traditions focus on one almost to the exclusion of the other. In the crisis corner are groups that emphasize an immediate, intense, emotional response: "Come to the altar, kneel, and pray. Weep as you throw a stick into the fire or plant your stake in the ground. Have a life-changing crisis." But when the intensity of the moment dies away, what happens to the decision that was made?

In the process corner are groups that promote gradual change and spiritual progress: "As you understand better, make better choices, and establish a better pattern, you'll find that change is gradual, never intense." But without a decisive interruption that creates a break with sin, what gets the healthy process started?

Both a crisis and a process are needed. Once you're through the crisis and into the process, if you fall to temptation, another crisis may be in order.

A crisis over sexual sin is required to break through the numbness—the depreciated capacity to be outraged by behavior that grieves the heart of God. The crisis gets our attention; provokes an emotional, willful response; and creates a turning point. The crisis we'll focus on this week is necessary, but alone it's not enough. Next week we'll continue with the process of getting unstuck from sexual sin.

When it comes to the subject of sexual sin, you may have never had a crisis. Or you may have had one before and need another one. Until you've had one, you won't see the need for the process of breaking free.

DAY 1
UNSTUCK MEANS CHANGE

This week we're focusing on the crisis that creates a recognition that someone is stuck in a pattern of sexual sin. As we begin week 3 of this Bible study, you may begin to notice a common theme. The study may be called *Unstuck,* but the lessons almost always begin with discovering that we can't get fresh traction for common struggles until we admit we've got a problem. Recognizing something is wrong doesn't solve the problem, but it sets in motion the possibility of identifying the issue and addressing it.

It would be difficult to overestimate how badly many people need a crisis about sexual sin in their lives. Immorality is ravaging our society, wrecking families, and destroying lives. The statistics are sickening. Behavior that used to cause people shame and was kept as a dark secret is now joked about on nightly television as though it's understood that such behavior is a part of everyone's sexual experience. Technology has made deviance from God's ideal accessible to people as never before in history, and every breakthrough in channels of communication is almost immediately infected with outlets for pornography, personal immorality, and inappropriate images that blur the line between sexual depravity and criminal acts involving children and unwilling participants. The cultural rot is deep and widely felt.

What comes to mind when you think about being in crisis? Describe your most recent crisis.

You may or may not feel comfortable recording the answer to this question. How has sexual sin directly or indirectly affected your life?

Sin affects every human being and ensures that few of us reach adulthood these days without being damaged by unhealthy sexuality in some way. Sexual behavior is often explained as the result of acts that were done to us or behaviors we were exposed to in younger years. But identifying the cause isn't an excuse. Realizing the way we were exposed to sexual sin doesn't relieve us from the need to do something about it. If sexual sin is present, it's time to consider whether a crisis is imminent or already present.

A crisis arrives when we fully admit that sexual sin, like all sin, violates God's commands.

> **Read Genesis 39:6b-10. Although Joseph mentioned the importance of maintaining integrity in his relationship with his employer, what was Joseph's ultimate reason for rejecting the offer of Potiphar's wife?**

> **Why should all sin produce a crisis for us?**

> **How does Joseph's example show us that the opportunity to sin sexually shouldn't lead us to commit that sin?**

Although we sometimes call the terrible things we do to others sins, the sin part actually refers to the fact that our actions have been an affront to God and have violated His instructions. Seeking to fulfill a good desire in a way other than how God intended is sin. Sex is a healthy, God-given desire meant to be fulfilled within the divinely designed parameters of marriage. The call to admit this (or any) sin should cause an internal crisis for us. In that moment either we embrace our sin and reject God, or we reject our sin and embrace God's best.

> **When and how has God brought you to a crisis over sin in your life?**

We have to realize that sin, and sexual sin in particular, puts us squarely in the position of being guilty before God. This fact exposes the reality of sin in so-called private and "victimless" behaviors like entanglement with pornography. God is fully aware of all sin, and it deeply offends His love for us and His desire to show us an abundant way of living.

Read 1 Corinthians 6:9-20. What significant hope does verse 11 offer after the devastating list of behaviors that prevent someone from inheriting the kingdom of God?

The crises we face are meant to lead us to the gospel. There we find forgiveness from all our sin and wrongdoing. Has that ultimate crisis occurred in your life? How and when?

How has the Lord changed you since you've become a follower of Jesus?

What patterns of sin has He broken in your life?

Spend a moment each day meditating on this week's memory verse:

Flee from sexual immorality. Every other sin a person commits is outside the body, but the sexually immoral person sins against his own body.
1 CORINTHIANS 6:18

What does fleeing from sexual immorality look like for you?

End this lesson by asking God to sensitize you to the crises He brings into your life as means of guiding you through the process of spiritual transformation He has planned for you.

DAY 2
CONFRONTING CONSEQUENCES

A painfully high percentage of people reading these words have been victims of sexual abuse in some fashion or another. If not, someone close to you has been. And it's tragic to discover how easily victims in one generation become perpetrators in the next. There's nothing casual, soft, or innocent about sexual sin. Once inside the door, mind, or heart, it's virulent, spreading into every area of life and into other lives. Nothing short of a God-ordained, Holy Spirit-provoked crisis will reach us and begin the changes we need to make progress in godliness.

The people we meet in the Bible, though they lived many centuries ago, faced the same core temptations we face. Joseph didn't have a television, but he knew about seduction. Samson didn't have access to the Internet, but he understood the drive to search for sexual excitement. Their experiences speak to ours with such clarity that the results often produce a crisis. The writer of Hebrews described the unique power of Scripture:

> *The word of God is living and active, sharper than any two-edged sword, piercing to the division of soul and of spirit, of joints and of marrow, and discerning the thoughts and intentions of the heart. And no creature is hidden from his sight, but all are naked and exposed to the eyes of him to whom we must give account.*
> **HEBREWS 4:12-13**

What's a personal example of a time when a particular verse or story from Scripture cut into your life like a scalpel?

Read Judges 16.

While the world typically insists on telling only the exciting, fun, and titillating aspects of violating God's instructions, Samson's story reveals the other side of sexual sins: the consequences. The fact is, when we choose to sin, we choose to suffer.

Identify from your reading the following consequences in Samson's life.

Loss of mission:

Loss of loyalty:

Loss of common sense:

Loss of fear:

Loss of God's favor:

Add a short phrase to each of the previous points that identifies how that loss occurred.

As Samson persisted in sin, how did his sinful behavior intensify?

Consequences are God's way of encouraging a crisis. If we keep pressing forward in folly, the painful results also escalate. In Samson's case it took blindness, humiliation, and slavery to bring him to the point of returning to God. For some of us, like the prodigal son, it takes a little less hardship to serve as a wake-up call.

Read the following verses and match them with the consequences they describe (one of the Scriptures applies to two consequences).
___ Numbers 32:23   a. Consequences are exponential.
___ Galatians 6:7   b. Exposure is certain.
___ Hosea 8:7   c. God isn't mocked.
**   d. Forgiveness doesn't erase consequences.**

The reality that forgiveness doesn't eliminate consequences is a sobering aspect of accountability before God. Forgiveness doesn't reverse the effects of the wrongs we've done. Though humbled and forgiven, Samson was still blind. The prodigal returned home to forgiveness but had to deal with a brother who was still hurt and angry. David's sins, though forgiven, unleashed a series of horrific events in his family. Tragically, consequences may continue to flow even after forgiveness has been granted.

God's grace covers our sin through forgiveness. Romans 8:1 says anyone who's in Christ is no longer condemned for past sins. Nevertheless, our past actions may echo through our lives for a long time.

What are some consequences you're having to live with now as a result of sexual sins or other sins that you've confessed to God and for which you've received forgiveness?

Ongoing consequences keep us humble and drive us to God for strength. Even though He's "faithful and just to forgive us our sins and to cleanse us from all unrighteousness" (1 John 1:9), consequences remind us that God's forgiveness isn't a get-out-of-jail-free card. We must respond to the realization of sin against God and seek His forgiveness apart from any immediate relief from the consequences of what we did. In days 3–5 we'll walk through the process of repenting, renouncing rationalizations, and making restitution for sexual sins. These parts of crisis set us on the course to being unstuck by clearing the way for the process God will use to bring change in our lives.

Spend a moment meditating on this week's memory verse:

Flee from sexual immorality. Every other sin a person commits is outside the body, but the sexually immoral person sins against his own body.
1 CORINTHIANS 6:18

Believers sin against our own bodies because the Holy Spirit indwells us and is present when we engage in immorality (see v. 19). Ephesians 4:30 warns us not to "grieve the Holy Spirit." When we hurt ourselves through sexual misconduct, we also hurt Him.

End this lesson in prayer, asking for the willingness to flee from sexual immorality into the arms of your Heavenly Father, who loves you.

DAY 3
REALIZATION AND REPENTANCE

Our almost instinctive initial response to the crisis of recognizing sin in our lives takes the form of regret. We feel bad about sin. We feel bad about being caught in sin. We hang our heads in shame and wish we could go back and do things over again. And all too often we mistake those feelings of regret for repentance. However, remorse, guilt, shame, and regret aren't repentance. They can lead to repentance; often they lead somewhere else. Repentance turns to God; regret can easily turn us away from God.

What is repentance? What did the Old Testament prophets, John the Baptist, Jesus Himself, and the apostles mean when they delivered one-word sermons: "Repent!"? Repentance is a recognition of sin, followed by heartfelt sorrow, culminating in a change of behavior. You come to your senses (mind), recognize your unworthiness (emotions), then plan and act differently (will). At its deepest level, repentance is turning from something (sin) in order to be able to turn toward something new (embracing Jesus Christ by faith).

RECOGNITION OF SIN	HEARTFELT SORROW	CHANGE OF BEHAVIOR
Mind	Emotions	Will
Turning from sin	→	*Turning toward Jesus*

Read the previous descriptions of *repentance* a couple of times. Why do you think God is interested in our repentance, not just our regret?

Knowing what repentance is doesn't mean we've repented. In the first moments of shock when we catch a glimpse of our condition as sinners, our enemy rushes in to keep us from repentance at all costs. He will either try to convince us that we're sinners beyond help and urge us to give up, or he will suggest that things aren't really as bad as they obviously seem at the moment. Satan's tactic of injecting hopelessness is one we must reject. We must move through our regret to genuine repentance.

Think for a moment about the two main figures involved when Jesus was betrayed and arrested: Judas and Peter. Peter, who couldn't imagine ever turning from Jesus, ended up disowning Him three times. Judas led a crowd to where he knew Jesus would be easy to capture. Both of these men regretted what they had done. Peter went out, wept bitterly, and remained tentative about his status until Jesus restored him in John 21. Judas, filled with remorse, took the money back to those who were engineering Jesus' death and then took his own life. The first repented; the second let regret overwhelm his life.

Peter's and Judas's crises were brought about by sin, which resulted in brokenness. What led these men to respond differently?

What experiences have you had that illustrate the difference between regret and repentance?

When you find yourself in this tension, how do you typically respond?

Read 2 Corinthians 7:8-11.

This is the key New Testament passage on repentance. Repentance is a sure sign that we're responding in the right way to a spiritual crisis.

In this passage how did Paul use the term *grief* to describe a crisis?

In verses 10-11 what attitudes did Paul identify that often accompany genuine repentance?

Whether you've been dabbling or drowning in sexual sin, the crisis God places before you is repentance. The prodigal son is the poster boy for repentance. Jesus told his story in Luke 15. The younger of two sons took his inheritance and ran away from his dad because he thought he knew better. He lived very high on the hog for a while until his money ran out, and then he ended up living with the hogs. When his crisis of repentance came, three changes occurred in him that affected his mind, emotions, and will. Notice how the prodigal experienced the marks of genuine repentance.

Read Luke 15:11-32.

THE PRODIGAL CHANGED HIS MIND. Life slapped him into a different way of thinking. Verse 17 says, "He came to himself." He woke up and could suddenly see the absolute mess in his life. What he had previously seen as attractive and freeing now sickened him. That response is characteristic of a change of mind, a different way of seeing.

THE PRODIGAL'S HEART WAS CHANGED. When he left home, he considered himself the center of the universe. Now he saw his insignificance. Even the servants in his father's house had life great compared to him. He knew he wasn't worthy to be called his father's son (see vv.17-19). God has to take some of us very low in order to teach us the right point of view.

THE PRODIGAL'S WILL KICKED IN. Even when he was still in the pigsty, he said, "I will arise and go to my father" (v. 18). He created a plan and put it into action. He didn't wallow in his situation or rationalize. He started the process by going home, with the stench of the hogs still on him. No pride, no expectations, just humility and a longing for forgiveness.

When was the most recent time God led you to repentance? When has this happened over areas of sexual sin?

What have been the outcomes of that response to God?

Spend a moment meditating on this week's memory verse:

Flee from sexual immorality. Every other sin a person commits is outside the body, but the sexually immoral person sins against his own body.
1 CORINTHIANS 6:18

End this lesson in stillness and silence, asking God to reveal areas of sin in your life. Repent and ask God to forgive you. Receive the forgiveness He freely offers.

DAY 4
RATIONALIZATION RADAR

Recognizing our sin causes grief and regrets, but it can also provoke rationalizations, which can quickly derail genuine repentance. Rationalizations are excuses or reasons we give to avoid accepting the truth that something we're doing is wrong. One mark of our sinful nature is our capacity to rationalize almost any behavior.

Satan is the master rationalizer, the one Jesus called "the father of lies" (John 8:44). Jesus knew this firsthand from His temptation in the wilderness (see Matt. 4:1-11), when three times the devil invited Him to rationalize an action that would have violated His purpose for coming to earth. The enemy even used Scripture as one of his tactics (see vv. 5-7). When we resort to twisting Scripture to validate our actions, we compound our offense against God by attempting to use His Word to get our way.

Read Matthew 4:1-11. What did Satan appeal to in each of the three temptations of Jesus?

1.

2.

3.

How could Jesus have rationalized cooperating with the devil in each of these cases?

What points did Jesus make in each of His responses?

As we can see even in the temptation of Jesus, most rationalization avoids Scripture and seeks to justify our wants and desires. Satan's first approach was based on hunger, a natural, necessary desire. It represents all hungers that Satan is ready to twist and present to us as worthy to be met by any means. The devil has made a career out of using legitimate, God-given appetites for food and sex to rationalize misuse, abuse, and self-destructive actions that have left people deeply trapped in sexual sin.

The third temptation focused on Jesus' purpose, offering Him instant success for the simple cost of worshiping Satan. Rationalizations often offer deceptive shortcuts to real desires. Pornography is a demonic shortcut presented as a quick, private, and completely self-centered satisfaction of desires that God intended us to satisfy only through the intimate, mutual sharing found in marriage.

> **Describe in one sentence how each of the following rationalizations might be used to avoid a needed crisis over sexual sin.**
>
> **1. I deserve this little benefit.**
>
> **2. This is just one of my weaknesses.**
>
> **3. I can handle this; it isn't affecting me.**
>
> **4. This is just for me, and no one will ever know.**
>
> **5. If only you knew my situation.**

Each rationalization seeks to excuse sin. Rationalization 1 is a *pleasure* excuse, actually translating sinful behavior into a reward that should rightly come to us. Rationalization 2 is a *personal* excuse that assumes right living in other ways accumulates moral equity so that a minor indiscretion can be overlooked. Rationalization 3 is a *prideful* excuse that acknowledges the danger but claims to maintain control with delusions like "I can stop anytime." Rationalization 4 is a *privacy* excuse, ignoring God's presence and failing to heed His warnings that all of life is eventually public (see John 3:19-21). Rationalization 5 represents a *pity* excuse, claiming hardship or unusual circumstances as the reason for sexual sin. None of these arguments avoid the chaos, the consequences, or God's ultimate judgment on the sinful behaviors they attempt to justify.

God isn't a cosmic killjoy, maliciously withholding things that would give us a better life. Rather, He's a loving Father who carefully protects us from the things that would destroy us. All that God forbids, He forbids as loving protection. All that God commends, He commends because He desires to bless us and give us good gifts. May God forgive our callous indifference to His law in our arrogant pursuit of the momentary satisfaction of sexual sin.

Which rationalization have you most often used to excuse sin in your life?

Why do we try to excuse our sin rather than deal head-on with the sorrow and heartbreak that sin produces?

Spend a moment meditating on this week's memory verse:

Flee from sexual immorality. Every other sin a person commits is outside the body, but the sexually immoral person sins against his own body.
1 CORINTHIANS 6:18

Based on this verse, record three ways you could respond when you're tempted to rationalize sexual sin.

1.

2.

3.

End this lesson by asking God to calibrate your rationalization radar and strengthen your resolve to flee from sexual immorality with His help.

DAY 5
THE ROLE OF RESTITUTION

When repentance is real, we reject rationalizations and pursue restitution. One tragic aspect of sexual sin is that restitution—making things right—is often incomplete at the human level. Adultery can't be undone. The time wasted in the pursuit of pornography can't be recaptured. Violated trust may take a long time, if ever, to rebuild. Nevertheless, genuine repentance moves from private to public and seeks reconciliation with those harmed by our sexual sin.

At the point of crisis, when God allows you to come to yourself in the brokenness of sexual sin, confession begins by acknowledging that you've first and deeply broken God's law. This was King David's discovery when Nathan used a story to bring his royal friend to a shattering crisis after the Bathsheba episode (see 2 Sam. 12:1-7a). In Psalm 51 David painstakingly wrote his confession to God. After repeatedly owning his actions ("my transgressions," "my iniquity," "my sin," vv. 1-2), David wrote:

> Against you, you only, have I sinned
>   and done what is evil in your sight,
> so that you may be justified in your words
>   and blameless in your judgment.

PSALM 51:4

David had Nathan to walk him through the crisis, but he also made things right directly with God. If the Holy Spirit is convicting you of sexual sin, you'll have the same experience as the prodigal, whose father embraced him with loving pardon even as the son was voicing his confession. Confess your sin to God and trust in His forgiveness (see 1 John 1:9). Take joy in realizing that God has brought this crisis to you and that He will be eagerly joining you in the process of getting unstuck.

If sometime during this study you've reached a crisis by recognizing that God was graciously drawing back the shutters on sin you've been hiding, don't miss this opportunity God is giving you to become unstuck from patterns of sin. Darkness always flees from light. Sin flees in the holiness of God's grace and mercy.

What stops you from taking your sin to God? Why is the freedom God offers from your sin better than the trap of sin?

Take a few minutes to read all of Psalm 51. Pray the verses that express your own sense of brokenness before your Heavenly Father.

As prodigals, we come to our Heavenly Father in confession and receive forgiveness; as prodigals, we also have to approach our flesh-and-blood relationships with confession. Once things are right between you and God, it's time to go public. The pattern is clear in the steps of salvation in Romans 10:

> *If you confess with your mouth that Jesus is Lord and believe in your heart that God raised him from the dead, you will be saved. For with the heart one believes and is justified, and with the mouth one confesses and is saved.*
> **ROMANS 10:9-10**

External confession seals our salvation and completes repentance in the area of specific sins. Our confession to others of sins we've already confessed to God doesn't affect His forgiveness of us, but it assures us of forgiveness and confirms our repentance. If we're unwilling to confess to another person, we cast doubt on the genuineness of our repentance.

Confession doesn't mean dragging others through the details of our sins. If speaking the specifics would cause further damage and inflict unnecessary pain, the sin can be confessed in general terms. The prodigal admitted his sins without detailing them. But humanly speaking, we all need someone in our lives who can listen to the ugliness of our sin and assure us of God's forgiveness. This is the point of James 5:16:

> *Confess your sins to one another and pray for one another, that you may be healed. The prayer of a righteous person has great power as it is working.*
> **JAMES 5:16**

Besides your spouse or a family member to whom you confess in general terms, what other person can you trust to listen to your unedited confession and pray for you?

If you have no one in that role, what will it take to find such a person?

Spend a moment meditating on this week's memory verse:

Flee from sexual immorality. Every other sin a person commits is outside the body, but the sexually immoral person sins against his own body.
1 CORINTHIANS 6:18

Based on this verse, you may also owe restitution to yourself. Because sexual sin involves your own body, you may need to take steps that put you so far from temptation that you no longer have to flee from it. For example, if an electronic device is your ready door to sexual immorality, you may have to remove that device or severely limit its use.

What measure(s) will you take to create distance between you and temptation?

If you struggled for clarity in this area, take your need for wisdom to God in prayer. Ask Him to lead you to obstacles and good pursuits that will create distance between you and triggers for sexual sin.

Repentance is the crisis that sets a process in motion, and it's a place we need to visit often since much of life is spent gaining traction as God does His lifelong work in us. That process is what we'll focus on next week.

WEEK 4
GETTING UNSTUCK FROM SEXUAL SIN: THE PROCESS

Welcome to session 4 of Unstuck.

Begin the group session with prayer. Invite God's Spirit to continue striving with members who are in crisis, to guide and encourage those who are confessing their sins, and to affirm those who've approached God for forgiveness.

In this session we're going to look at the other aspect of the change required to get unstuck from sexual sin. We've looked at the crisis. Now we're on to the process.

Use some or all of the following questions to prepare the group for the video teaching.

> **Based on the previous group session or your personal study this week, how would you summarize a crisis?**
>
> **Why are crises a crucial part of change?**
>
> **If you've followed Jesus for a while, you may have developed a pattern of sin, confess, sin, confess, sin, confess that hasn't brought about lasting change. What's the difference between going through the motions of confession and expressing true repentance?**
>
> **Describe a time when you experienced the peace of receiving God's forgiveness.**

This week's teaching picks up where we left off last week with the nature of repentance and the steps of confession. There's a fine line between the crises we experience and the process God is using to work in our lives. It's crucial to understand both.

WATCH

Use this guide to follow along as you watch video session 4.

Five Steps in the Process of Getting Unstuck from Sexual Sin

1. I must seek God daily and fervently.

2. I must eliminate the opportunity to fail.

3. I must make myself truly accountable.

4. I must cultivate healthy sexuality.

5. I must occupy my time with purpose and fulfillment.

Drastic Actions for a Life-Giving, Healthy Marriage

1. No unfiltered access to the Internet

2. No unblocked channels on the television

3. No unaccountable time

Levels of Accountability

1. Accountability for honesty

2. Accountability for total honesty

3. Accountability for obedience

4. Accountability for the consequences of disobedience

Agreed-upon Consequences

1. Loss of freedom

2. Loss of confidentiality

3. Loss of relationship

How to Fall Flat on Your Face

1. Prosperous times

2. Passive wills

3. Overpowering emotions

4. Impure thoughts

5. Private sin

6. Public consequences

Fulfillment Alternatives

1. Ministry   2. Activity   3. Family   4. Education   5. Work

Video sessions available at lifeway.com/unstuck
or with a subscription to smallgroup.com

Discuss the video teaching with your group.

Freedom from sin begins with confession. How do confession and transparency with others break the cycle of sin, confession, and recurring sin as nothing else can?

Summarize the five steps in the process that can address the issue of sexual sin after repentance.

Read 2 Samuel 11:1-2; Psalm 63:1; Proverbs 27:6,9; Romans 13:11-14; and 1 Corinthians 7:1-5. Identify which verse applies to each step in becoming unstuck from sexual sin.

Pastor James discussed several levels of accountability. What stood out to you in that teaching?

What questions do you have about any steps in the process of getting traction in the area of sexual sin? Do you have concerns you'd like the group to pray about?

If repentance isn't a regular feature of our lives, what aren't we believing about the gospel?

APPLICATION. Using the five steps in the process Pastor James taught, give yourself a grade for each step, from 1 (never practice) to 5 (consistently practice). Record one step you'll take this week to improve one of your grades.

THIS WEEK'S MEMORY VERSE
Confess your sins to one another and pray for one another, that you may be healed. The prayer of a righteous person has great power as it is working.
JAMES 5:16

ASSIGNMENT. Complete this week's personal study before the next group session. Make notes of any questions you want to discuss with other group members. Pray for each member of your group by name, asking the Holy Spirit to give them a fresh vision of the process He's using to help them gain traction in their lives.

SLIPPERY ROAD AHEAD

In all change there's first a crisis and then a process. Crisis is getting stuck and knowing it; process is regaining traction. Crisis is meeting Christ; process is knowing and living for Christ. Crisis is repenting of sexual sin; process is practicing intentional steps to repent, assure ourselves of forgiveness, and pursue healthy relationships and spiritual growth. When we fail in the process, we must return to the crisis. This week we'll examine the process that follows the crisis of sexual sin.

The crisis of repentance is a necessary step in real transformation, but repentance isn't the final step in change; it's just the first step. And it leads to the process of ongoing repentance, which involves continued confession. The call to repentance is the call of a prophet; the call to the process requires the tone of a pastor and teacher, instructing, by God's grace, the Lord's people in the process of change.

James 5:16 says, "Confess your sins to one another and pray for one another, that you may be healed." You might still think, *Why would we confess our sins to one another? Scripture is clear that only God can forgive sins.* But there's a reason God's Word tells us to confess to one another.

We repent and confess our sins to God for forgiveness. We don't confess our sins to one another for forgiveness. We confess our sins to one another for the *assurance* of forgiveness. When patterns of sin are greatly ingrained, when sin, confess, sin, confess has become a too-often-repeated cycle, engagement with our brothers and sisters in Christ, mutually acknowledging sin and soliciting God's help to break that pattern, is the biblical prescription. It's a lifelong process.

Based on last week's study, I hope you'll approach this week with a heart filled with repentance, genuine regret, and godly grief over sinful sexual choices and its consequences. At the same time, however, maybe you sincerely regret things you've done, things you've thought, things you've seen, and choices you've made. But when you come to the crisis and the train stops at Sexual-Temptation City, you always get off the train. So going forward, when you approach the station, how do you make a different choice and stay on the train that's headed for a better destination?

That's the challenge we want to address with truth and hope from God's Word this week.

DAY 1
A DAILY PROCESS

As we learned last week, change begins with a crisis. That's true in overcoming any sinful addictive pattern, including sexual addiction. There must be a crisis; a turning; or, as the Bible frequently states it, repentance. If last week's study got your attention, broke a pattern, and drove you to Christ, this week's lessons will be crucial.

> **Take a moment to consider good things God has done in your life. In what areas of life would you say you've found victory over past sins?**
>
> **What did God teach you in the process of overcoming those areas of weakness?**

This entire study is subtitled *Fresh Traction for Common Struggles.* The word *common* isn't referring just to the fact that people all around us face the same problems we have. It also means we have these struggles in common with people throughout history. First Corinthians 10:13 reminds us:

> *No temptation has overtaken you that is not common to man. God is faithful, and he will not let you be tempted beyond your ability, but with the temptation he will also provide the way of escape, that you may be able to endure it.*
> **1 CORINTHIANS 10:13**

Before we turn to our peers for help in living the Christian life, we'd be wise to observe the lives of biblical men and women for time-proven practices and ways of escape that God has provided for us to endure and overcome temptation.

If we interviewed the people who populate the Bible and the cloud of believing witnesses in church history about the way to resist temptation and experience the process of spiritual growth, they would answer with one voice, "Seek God daily and fervently." The heroes of our faith weren't perfect. Sometimes they failed in spectacular fashion, but they also knew and walked with God. Job spoke for many of them who faced very difficult situations yet with faith said of God, "Though he slay me, I will hope in him" (Job 13:15).

Read Psalm 63:1. What did the psalmist say about himself and about God in this verse?

How would you describe the relationship summarized in that verse?

Read these intimate biblical testimonies about seeking God: Psalms 9:10; 14:2; 27:8; 34:10; 40:16; 105:3-4.

How would you describe the tone of these passages?

What do these passages say about the person seeking God?

What do they say about God and His response to being sought by us?

Read James 4:7-8a. How are the first and third commands different from the second?

What happens as we obey each command?

We sometimes have the idea that a strong, vibrant faith is something handed to a select group of chosen people. Yet the Scriptures teach that a strong, dynamic walk with Christ comes from intentionally seeking God. From Jesus in the wilderness (see Matt. 4:1-11) to every other victor in the Scriptures, the power of God's Word in facing temptation is clearly evident in their lives. If you want to get unstuck and remain free from sexual sin, you need to have weapons, and God's Word is the sword (see Eph. 6:17). You need to have it hidden in your heart, the overflow of your seeking the Lord daily. You'll be amazed by the strength that's ignited in your soul when you passionately seek the Lord, memorize His Word, and use it to determine at the beginning of your day what your life purpose is going to be.

Throughout this study you've been asked to memorize one verse each week. If you've committed to this practice, how have you already benefited from memorizing God's Word?

What Scripture could you memorize to speak to your specific struggles and crisis points?

Seeking God is the furnace that fuels the fire of victory over sexual sin. By spending time with God, we can tear down the altar of selfishness and fleshly desires, and we can raise in its place the altar that proclaims the supremacy of Jesus Christ, His glory, and His purposes in this world.

Intimacy with Jesus is nurtured when we begin to seek Him daily though His Word and pursue biblical spiritual disciplines. If we begin the day without exalting Jesus to His rightful place, how can we expect that when temptation comes, we'll be able to resist it without His help? Any process to root out patterns of sin in our lives begin with Jesus. We have to know Him and live for His approval and praise. Knowing we're fully loved and accepted by Christ moves us to deny our sin in order to follow Him (see Matt. 16:24).

How will you connect with God today?

Spend a moment meditating on this week's memory verse:

Confess your sins to one another and pray for one another, that you may be healed. The prayer of a righteous person has great power as it is working.
JAMES 5:16

Who knows you well enough to pray about what really matters in your life? How would sharing God's ongoing work with someone else help you grow in your relationship with God?

DAY 2
ESTABLISHING BOUNDARIES

The next step in the process of spiritual growth that will help us overcome sexual sin is to monitor our level of temptation. We can't live in or near a mudhole and expect not to get dirty. Too often we allow the means of temptation to be all too accessible to us.

Because Satan never takes a break and our flesh doesn't stop seeking its own pleasures, we sometimes feel as though failure is inevitable. However, the Bible gives us practical guidance for establishing boundaries that can keep sexual sins at a distance.

Read Romans 13:11-14. Was Paul speaking to people who were saved or unsaved? Why does this make a difference?

What six specific "works of darkness" (v. 12) did Paul instruct his readers to stay away from?

What six positive actions did Paul urge in these verses, and what does each of them mean? For example, what might he have had in mind by saying, "The hour has come for you to wake from sleep" (v. 11) as a way to establish boundaries for sin?

How does the statement "Make no provision for the flesh, to gratify its desires" (v.14) describe an effective deterrent to past patterns of sexual sin?

Of the six destructive behaviors Paul listed in verse 13 under the category of "works of darkness" (v. 12), half involve sexual immorality. It's not surprising that the enemy would tempt us to flout God's instructions in that area.

The six positive actions Paul included in these verses are more general, reflecting the kind of freedom we have in Christ. They begin with an appeal to "wake from sleep," implying that Paul's readers were spiritually nodding off and inattentive in their spiritual lives. The next two are a set of matching actions: deliberately removing "works of darkness," which he then listed, and putting on "the armor of light" (v. 12). Here the word *armor* literally means "weapons of light," providing a strong contrast to darkness and suggesting truth and transparency. Next we're to "walk properly as in the daytime" (v. 13), with nothing to hide or be ashamed of, like works of darkness. Our primary purpose is to "put on the Lord Jesus Christ" (v. 14), seeking to increasingly display externally the truth of Christ's Spirit dwelling in us. We imitate Him when we "make no provision for the flesh" (v. 14). Jesus was surrounded by temptations, but He never violated the boundaries He had in place.

Most of us don't reach adulthood without a pretty clear idea of where the danger of sexual sin lies in wait for us. Technology has made temptation far more aggressive and invasive in our lives. Here are three specific sin gateways that require boundaries and perhaps padlocks.

1. **NO UNFILTERED ACCESS TO THE INTERNET.** Willingly use blockers or tattlers to regulate online usage.

2. **NO UNBLOCKED TV CHANNELS.** Entrust only one person with the unlock code.

3. **NO UNACCOUNTABLE TIME.** Make your schedule known to several trusted people who can track your location at any time.

   What are the benefits of setting these boundaries?

   Which of these ideas might help you create sexual-sin boundaries? Why?

Creating healthy boundaries helps us live above reproach. The purpose of boundaries isn't to constrict but rather to allow trust and freedom within limits. People who want to live in defeat or to protect their autonomy and ability to do whatever they want whenever they want would hate electronic boundaries. But if you're serious about victory over sexual sin, you'll make no provision for the flesh.

Guarding against temptations to fail sexually is central to living in the process of spiritual growth that God has designed for us. Embrace healthy patterns to get unstuck from sexual sin.

What are the primary boundaries you've established to keep your life free from sexual sin?

Based on the group session and your personal study this week, what boundaries might you need to create?

Though the topic of the week is sexual sin, how could boundaries in other areas help with additional sin struggles?

Spend a moment meditating on this week's memory verse:

Confess your sins to one another and pray for one another, that you may be healed. The prayer of a righteous person has great power as it is working.
JAMES 5:16

What kind of responsibility do you feel when another believer confesses a sin to you? How do you handle that responsibility?

As you end in prayer, ask God to bring to mind one person in your small group who seems to be struggling with these lessons. Take time to pray for them by name, asking God to continue His good work in them.

DAY 3
THE PROTECTION OF ACCOUNTABILITY

Yesterday's study introduced the principle of accountability. Today we want to delve into this matter more deeply because it's a natural outgrowth of this week's memory verse:

> *Confess your sins to one another and pray for one another,*
> *that you may be healed. The prayer of a righteous person*
> *has great power as it is working.*
> **JAMES 5:16**

When meditating on and applying a verse, it's important to know where the verse comes from to prevent misquoting or misusing Scripture. The immediate context of this verse includes verses 13-20, which picture the highs and lows of life together as followers of Jesus. Suffering is to be handled with prayer; good times are to be celebrated in worship and praise. Sin and the possible sickness that accompanies it are to be remedied through caring treatment and concerted prayer by church leaders. Then verse 16 presents the crucial importance of transparency so that our prayers for one another will be effective. In other words, we can't very well bring fellow believers' needs before God if we aren't being truthful with one another about them.

> **Read James 5:13-20. In what ways do these verses hold you accountable to other believers?**

In general, accountability refers to a system that ensures a responsible person will answer for his or her actions. The system includes a standard or set of expectations and someone who's designated to meet those expectations. The Bible frequently points out that our understanding and practice of accountability before God will be seen in the way we treat one another. The greatest example is found in a conversation between Jesus and a Jewish scribe in Mark 12:28-34, which began with an honest question: "Which commandment is the most important of all?" (v. 28). Basically, He was asking the Son of God, "How would You boil down our accountability to one thing, Lord?" Jesus answered with a two-part summary command, directed vertically and expressed horizontally.

Read Mark 12:28-34. What does it mean to be vertically accountable? What about horizontally?

The Bible is full of specific, practical examples of the accountability implications of loving our neighbor as ourselves, particularly our neighbors who are brothers and sisters in Christ.

Read Proverbs 27:6,9. According to these two proverbs, what are significant marks of real friendship?

How is the biblical ideal of friendship different from the world's?

Record a couple of examples of faithful wounds that true friends deliver.

These verses make it clear that in our common struggle with sexual sin, we're not going to get unstuck and gain traction unless we cultivate more biblical friendships and less enabling friendships. The former relationships emphasize mutual confession and holding one another accountable before God; the latter ones emphasize going along with whatever feels good while avoiding accountability.

But even as we develop biblical friendships, we need to realize that certain levels of accountability must be cultivated for full protection and growth.

DISCLOSURE AND REPENTANCE IN ACCOUNTABILITY SETTINGS. Coming clean about failures and shortcomings sets up accountability, but without repentance, correction, and direction, the process is short-circuited.

HONESTY IN ACCOUNTABILITY. We admit not only what we did wrong but also our motives and attitudes. We disclose rationalizations and reject them.

OBEDIENCE IN ACCOUNTABILITY. We give others permission to hold us account-able to make necessary changes. We ask for counsel on how to avoid making provision for the flesh in our lives.

ACCEPTED CONSEQUENCES FOR DISOBEDIENCE IN ACCOUNTABILITY. We give others permission to forcefully intervene and interrupt bad behavior and encourage right actions. Consequences might include loss of freedom or privileges ("We can't be with you until you make this right"), loss of confidentiality ("You've done some-thing illegal that we must report"), or loss of relationship ("You've removed yourself from our group"). For an example of consequences, read the way Paul addressed persistent sexual sin among the Corinthians (see 1 Cor. 5:1-5).

> **Review the levels of accountability and identify which one describes your default comfort zone in relation to other believers.**

> **How can you develop a deeper level of accountability with someone of the same gender in your Bible-study group?**

> **Meditate again on this week's memory verse:**

> *Confess your sins to one another and pray for one another, that you may be healed. The prayer of a righteous person has great power as it is working.*
> **JAMES 5:16**

> **Close your eyes and attempt to say the verse from memory. Which level of accountability best reflects the truth of this verse? Why?**

> **As you end today's assignment, pray that your group sessions will be marked by increasing levels of accountability, starting with you.**

DAY 4
PURSUING HEALTHY SEXUALITY

From God's wise perspective, healthy sexuality outside marriage requires abstinence from sex while pursuing Christlike character development (see 2 Tim. 2:22). And healthy sexuality within marriage means both partners are engaged in meeting each other's needs in both body and soul. When our culture talks about sexuality, it heavily emphasizes the physical aspects of sexual engagement. But as any married person quickly learns, sexuality actually involves every aspect of a person—body, mind, emotions, and spirit. The kind of oneness that God had in mind in Genesis 2:24 definitely includes sex but also every other aspect of a relationship. That kind of oneness is interesting and challenging enough to occupy a lifetime.

Because we're outlining the process that follows the crisis of repentance over sexual sin, it's important to acknowledge that this recovery process may be occurring after great damage has been done. Outside help from a pastor or a counselor is probably unavoidable. Returning to things as normal or as they were may not be an option, because what was previously happening was dysfunctional. The past by itself, therefore, may not offer much direction for the future. Fortunately, we can look to God's Word for direction.

If we've faithfully carried out the earlier steps we've covered, which may take time, our mate may have observed changes in us. If our earlier expression of repentance and request for forgiveness have been granted, we've initiated a crisis and process in our mate's life. Forgiveness may take time to take root and grow, while trust may take even longer to resume. Genuine repentance on our part will include giving our spouse time for this process.

We can begin moving toward normalizing sex under God's guidance by asking our marriage partner to join us in the steps of seeking God daily and fervently, establishing boundaries, and increasing mutual accountability. By inviting God into our relationship, we get to know each other in a new, deeper way. Seeking God together almost inevitably draws two people into closer intimacy.

Moving forward in the process requires understanding God's idea of healthy sexuality.

Read 1 Corinthians 7:1-5. Record three personal observations from these verses.

1.

2.

3.

In what specific ways do these verses hold you accountable?

What changes will eventually have to occur in your relationship for it to conform to the pattern of healthy sexuality described in these verses?

Do you see how the couple works together in these verses? What she wants, what he wants, when he wants, and how she wants all function in submission to one another. Neither spouse is the demanding party. Neither rules over the other. Mutual you-before-me love undergirds all healthy marital relationships.

Hebrews 13:4 says, "Let marriage be held in honor among all, and let the marriage bed be undefiled." A healthy view of marriage includes sexuality as central in it. Dietrich Bonhoeffer said, "It is not your love that sustains the marriage, but from now on, the marriage that sustains your love."[1] What a wise contradiction to everything our culture claims about marriage!

In marriage, staying together and negotiating everything that matters in the relationship help us learn to place the other person and their needs above our own. When both partners are committed to that, they create a beautiful place where love grows in ways they couldn't even imagine on their wedding day.

Think about your sexual expectations in marriage. Are you and your spouse on the same page? How does either of you need to make concessions to serve the other?

Three words summarize the nature of God's view of healthy marital sexual relations: *active, frequent,* and *fervent.* Nothing protects your marriage from sexual sin like healthy sexuality.

- *Active* means we're fully engaged—both body and soul. When that happens, the other two follow.

- *Frequency* means each couple has to find a happy medium of sexual activity in each season of life. At times more sex can become a dominant, destructive force in the marriage. Sex is a part of marriage, but it's not the totality of marriage. God's Word makes it clear that although sex is an important gift in life, it's not the primary focus of life.

- *Fervency* means your passion and attention are actively focused on your spouse.

For intimate glimpses of what these three concepts might look like in a marriage, check out the Song of Solomon in the Old Testament. Scripture has an amazing capacity to be clear about sex without being crass, voyeuristic, or overly descriptive.

Ask your mate to evaluate your marriage, based on the three previous criteria. Carefully listen to what he or she says in response. Practice active listening and repeat exactly what they said: "What I heard you say is ..." Don't offer your answer to the question until you're sure you understand what your partner said and meant.

Clarifying and agreeing on your current happy medium is actually a minicrisis. The process will be the way you move toward that happy medium together.

As you end this day's lesson, meditate on this week's memory verse, asking God to help you increase transparency with your marriage partner as you faithfully pray for him or her:

Confess your sins to one another and pray for one another, that you may be healed. The prayer of a righteous person has great power as it is working.
JAMES 5:16

1. Dietrich Bonhoeffer, *Letters and Papers from Prison,* ed. Eberhard Bethge (New York: Touchstone, 1953).

DAY 5
BEWARE OF VACUUMS

Unassigned time or unguarded activities create room for temptations to take our minds and hearts captive. To stay on track in the process of spiritual change and recovery from sexual sin, we must occupy our time with purpose and genuine fulfillment.

Throughout this study we've repeatedly noted that spiritual warfare is being waged behind the scenes (see Eph. 6:12). Sexual sins are the result of our choices and our flaws, but an enemy is also at work in the wings, doing all he can to ensure that we fall. Jesus made a startling point about why evil that's not completely dealt with has a way of coming back with a vengeance.

> **Read Matthew 12:43-45. In Jesus' description, what's the difference between just removing an evil spirit and replacing the spirit with something wholesome and true?**

Sexual sin, like all sinful behavior, hasn't been destroyed until the time and resources that were once invested in it are now fully engaged elsewhere. Turning away from sin without turning all the way toward Christ leaves us vulnerable to more destructively returning to our former sin. Incomplete repentance makes repeating a mistake almost certain. Because we're all recovering sinners in one way or another, our lives must focus on following Jesus and never drift without purpose.

The classic, tragic Bible story that illustrates this truth comes from the life of David, who, at the height of his rule as king, allowed himself to neglect his duties and spend an evening "channel surfing" on his rooftop terrace. As he looked over the neighborhood near the palace, he caught sight of a beautiful woman bathing in the open air, apparently oblivious to the fact that she had a royal audience.

> **Read 2 Samuel 11:1-5. What steps did David take between deciding to stay in Jerusalem and receiving the news that Bathsheba was pregnant?**

Some choices set events in motion that can be reversed; others bring irreversible consequences. What was that point in David's relationship with Bathsheba?

David's experience can be described as a series of danger points that we should stay alert to in our own lives.

PROSPERITY AND ACHIEVEMENT CAN LEAD TO PASSIVITY AND INATTENTION. When the process of recovery from sexual sin is having positive effects, we can't afford to slack off and take a break. That's because:

PASSIVITY MAKES US VULNERABLE TO UNEXPECTED OR STRONG EMOTIONS. Resting is important, but dropping our guard leaves us open to attack.

THE ATTACK MAY COME IN THE FORM OF AN IMPURE THOUGHT, A PICTURE, OR ANOTHER SUBTLE STIMULUS. We might think channel surfing or unfiltered Internet browsing is a harmless relief from boredom, but we're flirting with disaster.

THE TRIP FROM BOREDOM TO PRIVATE SIN CAN BEGIN IN A BLINK OR WITH A CLICK. In an instant, boundaries can be smashed, trust can be trashed, and a healing relationship can be reinjured.

MORE OFTEN THAN NOT, THE DESTINATION IS PUBLIC HUMILIATION OR A LIFE CONTROLLED BY THE FEAR OF EXPOSURE.

If we're serious about remaining unstuck from sexual sin and preserving traction in our lives, we need to find alternatives that occupy our attention and give purpose to our efforts. Serving the Lord in ministry, pursuing hobbies, engaging in meaningful times with family, discovering or improving a skill, embarking on a study to deepen our knowledge of Scripture, and finding work that fits our interests and abilities are all avenues that can help us avoid slippery places in our lives.

Which of the options you just read are on your list of go-to activities? Which would you be willing to explore? What else have you found that's profitable for investing your time?

Understanding the principle of crisis and process is a priceless tool in navigating the realities of spiritual life in a fallen world. Ideally, after experiencing a deep, thorough crisis, we then move on to the process. But if we think about the complexities of life, we'll realize that God is tracking multiple crisis-process projects in our lives at any one time. Yet we're never alone. This verse reminds us that once we've entrusted our lives to Christ, His Spirit is our partner every step of the way:

> *I am sure of this, that he who began a good work in you*
> *will bring it to completion at the day of Jesus Christ.*
> **PHILIPPANS 1:6**

The truth is that on the way to completion, we'll experience setbacks. When we fail in the process, we have to go back to the crisis and repent. James 3:2 is right: "We all stumble in many ways." Any believer who's a mature follower of Jesus will tell you their confidence is in Christ and His persistent willingness to forgive and lift them when they fall. We can always pick up the process again, once we've passed through the crisis and met Jesus again at the foot of the cross.

Why should the cross be the focus of all our repentance? How can it encourage us in our struggles?

If God has been leading you to a crisis over sexual sin, don't put off repentance. Go before Him in prayer and stay there until you're broken before Him. He will receive your confession and forgive. But now that you know the power of horizontal confession, don't stop until you've shared your experience with a brother or a sister in Christ:

> *Confess your sins to one another and pray for one another,*
> *that you may be healed. The prayer of a righteous person*
> *has great power as it is working.*
> **JAMES 5:16**

Pray that your fellow group members will benefit from God's instructions for dealing with sexual sin and will be able to overcome the obstacles they struggle with.

WEEK 5
GETTING UNSTUCK FROM FEAR

Welcome to session 5 of Unstuck.

Begin with a brief prayer acknowledging the challenges of the past two weeks and thanking God for the traction He has given to group members. Ask for wisdom on behalf of the group as you encourage one another to face crises and to persevere in the process of spiritual growth that God is working in your lives.

Share a victory or a significant discovery during the first four weeks of the study.

Use some or all of the following questions to prepare the group for the video teaching.

The topic for this week is getting unstuck from fear. When you were growing up, what were some things you thought were scary?

Can you think of something you were once afraid of but aren't now? How did that change happen?

What are some tasks or circumstances that still cause fear, but you face them anyway?

When it comes to common struggles, fears definitely fit the category. Pastor James will teach us from God's Word about gaining traction in this familiar experience.

WATCH

Use this guide to follow along as you watch video session 5.

Fear

A distressing emotion aroused by the anticipation of pain or harm or loss

If you're afraid of anything in an ongoing way, that's not from God.

You have nothing to fear.

You don't have to fear circumstances; you have power.

A whole generation had to die off because of fear.

The Spirit of Fear

1. Embrace the negative.

2. Enlarge the enemy.

3. Engage your fear.

Fear is a way of handling what felt like too much.

The Spirit of Power

1. Embrace the promise.

2. Enlist the support.

3. Exercise your faith.

The spirit of power obliterates opposing forces and powerfully overcomes and superconquers through Christ.

For circumstances God gives us power. For relationships He gives us love.

God made us with a need and a capacity for love.

Where I am fearing the fallout of relational failure, the fix, for sure, is love.

Video sessions available at lifeway.com/unstuck or with a subscription to smallgroup.com

Discuss the video teaching with your group.

> Pastor James's definition of *fear* is "a distressing emotion aroused by the anticipation of pain, harm, or loss." How closely does this definition match your experience? What would you add to or remove from it?

> Respond to this statement by Pastor James: "If fear is related to something that's actual, it's good. And it's from God. But most often when we're fearful, it's not because of something present and certain but because of something that's future and uncertain."

> Why is it important to recognize that our capacity for fear is from God?

> Pastor James connected each of the three words *power, love,* and *self-control* to a particular situation in which fear might be present: circumstances, relationships, and thought life. How was that explanation helpful?

> What are the three characteristics of the spirit of fear and the spirit of power? Why are these helpful to know?

> Why do you think the apostle Paul said love, even compared to faith and hope, is the greatest attribute (see 1 Cor. 13:13)? How does that fact confront fear?

APPLICATION. Love never fails, so if we fear the fallout of relational failure, the sure solution is love. When all the world stands against us, we're secure in Christ because of our relationship with Him through the gospel. Identify at least three relationships in which you're asking God for greater wisdom in expressing love.

THIS WEEK'S MEMORY VERSE

> *God gave us a spirit not of fear but of power and love and self-control.*
> **2 TIMOTHY 1:7**

ASSIGNMENT. Complete this week's personal study before the next group session. Make notes of any questions you want to discuss with other group members. Pray for each member of your group by name, asking the Holy Spirit to deal powerfully with their fears this week.

SLIPPERY ROAD AHEAD

We can all relate to fear in one form or another. It's a primal emotion, instinctive to our human nature just like grief or anger. You don't ever say to yourself, *I think I need to get afraid.* You don't have to plan it; fear just happens to you.

Of course, the problem isn't when fear stops by for a visit. The sudden, unexpected sounds or scenes that trigger the flight-or-fight instinct usually last for only as long as it takes to realize that the cause wasn't a real threat. Our heart rate soon returns to normal.

The real problem is when you open the front door and invite fear in. "Fear! Welcome back! I've been waiting for you. Your room is ready down the hall! No, I insist; take the master bedroom! *Mi casa es su casa!*" When you let fear take up residence in your mind, heart, and life and nourish it like a friend, that's a problem.

Although you can't keep fear from visiting, you can usher it out and slam the door in its face. And according to God's promises, that's exactly what you're able to do.

The sad reality is that too many Christians are victims of a pattern of thinking known as fear. Let's nail down a definition as we head into our study this week:

> **Fear:** *a distressing emotion aroused by the anticipation of pain, harm, or loss*

Throughout this week's studies we'll continually seek to respond to fear with God's presence and His Word, using this week's memory verse as our theme:

> *God gave us a spirit not of fear but of power and love and self-control.*
> **2 TIMOTHY 1:7**

DAY 1
UNDERSTANDING FEAR

Our capacity to be afraid is God-given. Part of our emotional makeup as human beings is the ability to experience distressing emotions aroused by the anticipation of pain, harm, or loss. Like anger or grief, fear is a gift to us, useful for specific purposes, but God never intended it to be the permanent setting of our lives. If we're afraid of anything in an ongoing way, that fear isn't from God.

Think about your fears. What are several examples of natural, helpful fears you have?

What fears do you have that are persistent and debilitating?

The Bible candidly acknowledges our human frailties. It mentions the overwhelming emotion of fear almost a thousand times. So 2 Timothy 1:7, this week's memory verse, identifies a common human condition when it gives us these words to live by:

God gave us a spirit not of fear but of power and love and self-control.
2 TIMOTHY 1:7

The word *spirit* in that verse can be misunderstood. Many times in the Bible, the word refers to the Holy Spirit. But the Holy Spirit isn't the only spirit mentioned in Scripture. In the New Testament the context determines when the word *spirit* refers to our spirit (our mind and emotions, our pattern of thinking) and when it refers to the Holy Spirit. In 2 Timothy 1:7 Paul was talking about our human spirit. If you have a fearful pattern of thinking, Paul was saying it's not from God.

What characterizes the spirit of fear that Paul had in mind? It's an attitude or a pattern of thinking that minimizes or dismisses God from having any impact on the cause of our fear. The Old Testament provides an amazing account of an entire generation that was infected with a spirit of fear. The people of Israel had left

Egypt, crossed the Red Sea on dry ground, miraculously survived in the wilderness, received the Ten Commandments, and arrived at the border of the promised land.

Read Numbers 13:1–14:38. Summarize the sequence of events in these two chapters. Highlight the places where a pattern of thinking that promoted fear is most apparent.

This is one of the most astounding tragedies in the entire Old Testament. The result was that a whole generation had to die before the nation could enter the promised land. Why? Because of fear. They settled into a spirit of fear. It was their default setting. It didn't really matter that God had moved on their behalf in amazing and great ways in the recent past; they looked into the future and didn't include God. So God excluded the people who didn't have the faith to go forward and embrace the blessings and the future He had promised.

From this account in Numbers, we can identify three characteristics of the spirit of fear that may be at work in your own life.

1. **A SPIRIT OF FEAR EMBRACES THE NEGATIVE.** It's apparent from this passage how quickly the Israelite nation reacted in abject fear to the news from the ten spies. The people insisted the cause was lost before the fight began. The ten had reported that the land God had promised flowed with milk and honey. But when they mentioned the downside, the people suddenly forgot the appealing features of the land. Caleb didn't waste any time; he went right for the locker-room charge: "Let us go up at once and occupy it, for we are well able to overcome it" (Num. 13:30). But the ten spies contradicted him, setting the tone for embracing the negative.

   Does this kind of reaction seem familiar to you? In what situations are you most prone to immediately take a dim, negative view of a situation?

2. **A SPIRIT OF FEAR ENLARGES THE ENEMY.** Suddenly the promised land was crawling with giants who lived in impregnable cities. The spies mentioned the inhabitants' names to highlight their fierce reputations, whereas they didn't mention God once in their report. And the larger they saw the enemies, the

smaller they saw themselves, until "we seemed to ourselves like grasshoppers, and so we seemed to them" (Num. 13:33). They belittled themselves so much that they believed they were insignificant.

A spirit of fear looks at obstacles with a magnifying glass that makes the obstacle or hurdle insurmountable and the opposition unconquerable. What a moment for God's Word to interrupt such thinking with the truth: "We are more than conquerors through him who loved us" (Rom. 8:37)!

In what instances have you made an enemy or a problem bigger than it was because of your fear?

3. **A SPIRIT OF FEAR ENGAGES YOUR WORST FEARS.** Not only is the threat magnified, but the outcome is also seen in the worst possible light. A pattern of fearful thinking kicks into overdrive. The people loudly declared that all hope for their future and their children's future was lost.

   The more fear sets in, the less rational we become. When have you found this statement to be true?

   Spend a moment meditating on this week's memory verse:

   God gave us a spirit not of fear but of power and love and self-control.
   2 TIMOTHY 1:7

God has endowed our spirit with three traits—power, love, and self-control— that are His chosen antidotes for our spirit of fear, our negative disposition, and our defeatist way of thinking.

   Turn 2 Timothy 1:7 into a grateful prayer, not only thanking God for His gift of power, love, and self-control but also asking for wisdom to understand and use these gifts in facing your fears this week.

DAY 2
FEARLESS CIRCUMSTANCES

We ended yesterday's study by naming three traits God has given us to counteract a spirit of fear: power, love, and self-control. Though these are inseparable characteristics, each operates more strongly in certain settings. The first of these means we don't have to fear circumstances, no matter how much they may seem to be out of control. God has given us a spirit of power to meet those challenges.

The term *circumstance,* by definition, refers to events that aren't entirely under our control. All the factors that make up our environment and experience at any moment could be called our circumstances. Whatever our circumstances are, we're in the middle of them right now.

List five or six circumstances in your life that may tempt you to fear.

When we think of fear as distressing emotions aroused by the anticipation of pain, harm, or loss, one word we can't overlook is *anticipation.* We don't fear what's past unless we think it's going to come back and bite us in the future. And we don't really fear the present. What we tend to fear is what we anticipate—the future, what's going to happen next.

We get a call from a child who doesn't sound right. We hear that our spouse's workplace has filed for bankruptcy. We get a message to call our doctor immediately. We don't know what's going to happen, but we're afraid of what might happen. The more we anticipate this unknown circumstance, the more terrified we become.

But those responses aren't what God expects from us. He has given us something to help us combat our fear of circumstances. We don't have to fear; we have God-given power.

Yesterday we read about a generation mowed down by circumstances when they had every reason to move ahead in a spirit of power. They had experienced God's power exercised on their behalf, but they ignored this vivid evidence. Caleb and Joshua urged them to rise up and take the promised land, but no voices were louder or images larger than the ones in their fearful spirits. So for the next forty years they wandered in the wilderness, dropping one by one along the way.

When we get to Joshua 1, there's a new sheriff in town and a new attitude about the promised land.

Read Joshua 1. Underline in your Bible or note here every verse in which "strong and courageous" is used.

Who said those words (it's not always God), and what was the intent? Why is it important in those circumstances?

Shifting away from a spirit of fear is like the transition from the old to the new generation in Israel. The previous generation didn't go to God but managed things its own way until, over time, fear took over. But in place of a spirit of fear, God offers a spirit of power to help us get unstuck from that pattern.

A SPIRIT OF POWER EMBRACES THE PROMISE. God has made some promises in His Word, and His intent is for you to live by those promises. Think of it this way. No matter what your real or imagined circumstances, God's promises are the surest thing around you. When you feel constant waves of fear crashing on the shore of your mind, you can respond, even audibly, "No! I don't have to think fearfully like this. This isn't the way God wants me to live. I don't have to be Mrs. Doomsday or Mr. Dark Clouds. I can trust God for better things ahead. I can believe God is going to be good and faithful."

Besides the promise of 2 Timothy 1:7, what other promises from God come to mind? Spend a few moments searching the Scriptures if some promises don't immediately come to mind.

A SPIRIT OF POWER ENLISTS THE SUPPORT OF OTHERS. As believers, we're not supposed to live our lives alone. And when we get together with Christians, we're not supposed to play a game of "I'm fine." We're supposed to pray together, encourage one another, and lean on God together (see Jas. 5:14-16). The spirit of power rejects the idea that isolation is survival.

What role do other Christians have in your life as you face fearful circumstances?

Why is prayer such an effective strategy to overcome our fears?

A SPIRIT OF POWER EXERCISES FAITH. When circumstances appear threatening, faith answers, "That's a lie. I'm going to believe I can handle this with God's help." Faith redefines and describes the circumstances with God in control. A spirit of power declares, "God said He will never leave me or forsake me. That's what He promised."

If you spend a couple of days living in God's Word, abiding in His truth, and meditating on His promises, you're going to find that fear will flee in a hurry. As a Christ follower, you don't have a spirit of fear; it's an echo of who you were before you came to Jesus. You have a spirit of power—an internal, God-given capacity to overcome. The spirit of power obliterates opposing forces and powerfully overcomes and conquers through Christ. That's the power God has given you.

What are some circumstances in your life that have induced fear, but now you're ready to exercise faith in these areas?

Spend a moment meditating on this week's memory verse:

God gave us a spirit not of fear but of power and love and self-control.
2 TIMOTHY 1:7

Ask God for a greater awareness of the spirit of power He has given you, particularly in the fearful circumstances that came to mind today.

DAY 3
FEARLESS RELATIONSHIPS

Yesterday we saw how our God-given spirit of power applies to fearful circumstances. Many times it's not the circumstances that are most intimidating to us; it's the people in the circumstances. For challenging relationships, God gives us a spirit of love. That's why Paul, laying out a fear-response list, wrote in 2 Timothy 1:7, "God gave us a spirit not of fear but of ... love." Love is the dimension of this list that plays out most clearly in our relationships with other people. Think about that. No relational problem that's bringing fear in your life can't be overcome and conquered with the love God gives us. Because you have love, you have nothing to fear relationally.

Why would love would be more effective than power in relationships?

Who are some people you walk with in a relationship of love? Who are some people you find it difficult to love?

God made you not just with a need *for* love; He also made you with a capacity *to* love. You even have a capacity to love people who are hard to love. You can treat others in loving ways that will enable you to feel love for them. When you love others with God's love, you don't have to fear running out. God has given you a supernatural capacity to love and to keep loving people.

Read Romans 8:16 and 1 John 4:7-20. What do these two passages tell you about the combined efforts of your spirit and God's Spirit to nurture love in your life as one of His children?

First John 4: 19 tells us that our basic understanding of love in this life begins with the way we've been loved by others. We can't love better than we've been loved. Our ability to love others increases in direct correlation to our realization that we've been loved by God. As we grow to realize the depth and constancy of His love, which He increasingly deposits in our spirit, we have a resource to tap in loving others.

In what ways are you relying on God's love for you and in you as you seek to love others, particularly people who cause you to feel fearful?

If you notice that you feel unloving or fearful toward others, what could that feeling indicate about your relationship with the Lord?

First Corinthians 13:13 says, "Faith, hope, and love abide, these three; but the greatest of these is love." Those are the big three: faith, hope, and love. Let's think about how they relate to one another. Faith is rooted in Christ and in His loving death on our behalf (see Rom. 5:1-8). Hope arises from our faith. Hope is a settled belief that things are going to get better and not worse. However, love is even better than hope. We wouldn't have hope without the love that sent Jesus Christ into this world. Love is the greatest gift. God poured it out for us and into us, and He designed it to flow through us into others.

You may be tempted to have a spirit of fear over turmoil in relationships when you don't know how a situation will turn out. Let Christ's love rise up in you and overcome what's been said to you, what's been done to you, or what's happened between you and that person.

Read 1 Corinthians 13:1-8. List the traits of love described there.

How closely does the way you love people match Paul's description?

The traits of love that are listed in 1 Corinthians 13 aren't homegrown capacities. They emanate from God. He has poured them into our spirit from the overflow of who He is. Because God has given us a spirit of love, we need to engage it in responding to our fears. The last of the traits is "Love never ends" (v. 8). Because love never fails, it offers the solution when you fear the fallout of relational failure. Only love will move you forward in that relationship.

Questions may arise in your mind: *What if they disappoint me? What if they hurt me?* Love them in spite of it and through it. They're going to hurt you, and you're going to keep loving them. God can use your love to change them and turn the relationship around. In the meantime, God will love you through that circumstance, and you'll know His love more deeply than ever before.

Read Romans 5:8. How did God love us when we were unlovable? What does the gospel teach us about the lengths to which we're called in order to love others?

What relationships in your life need a fresh experience of God's filling your spirit with love?

Spend a moment meditating on this week's memory verse:

God gave us a spirit not of fear but of power and love and self-control.
2 TIMOTHY 1:7

When have other people exercised a spirit of love to make a difference in your life?

As you end today's lesson, pray again for the person leading this study. Ask God to strengthen their spirit of love as they help others learn to get unstuck from fear.

DAY 4
FEARLESS THINKING

As we've addressed fear in circumstances and in relationships, the reality of the invisible battles in our minds has been a constant part of the picture. In fact, we began this week's study by recognizing that when applied to us, the word *spirit* can mean our attitude or disposition. The battle with fear is often won or lost, not because of an overwhelming circumstance or a dysfunctional relationship but in our minds. So we find that in Paul's list of the qualities of the spirit God has given to us, the sequence takes us progressively deeper and closer to the core of who we are as Christ followers. Paul wrote:

> *God gave us a spirit not of fear but of power and love and self-control.*
> **2 TIMOTHY 1:7**

Instead of *self-control*, some translations use *sound mind* (NKJV) or *self-discipline* (NIV). Actually, that word is difficult to translate. It's used sixteen times in the New Testament. In Mark 5:15 it describes a person who's no longer demon-possessed but in their right mind. In Acts 26:25 Paul denied charges of insanity by using this word, saying his words were sober truth, or spoken from right-mindedness. And in 1 Peter 4:7 the word is used to describe the kind of clearheaded judgment that's needed to pray at the end of the world.

What responses indicate to you that you're operating from a sound mind?

Clear, self-controlled thinking doesn't come naturally to us. That's why self-control is listed among the fruit of the Spirit (see Gal. 5:23). True discipline comes in taking our thoughts captive and submitting them to Christ (see 2 Cor. 10:5). If we're to become fearless in our thinking, our minds must be transformed:

> *Do not be conformed to this world, but be transformed by the renewal of your mind, that by testing you may discern what is the will of God, what is good and acceptable and perfect.*
> **ROMANS 12:2**

Notice the way Paul framed this command. Believers are to stop being conformed to the world and start being transformed by the renewal of their minds. The world we live in provides many opportunities to descend into fear. Adapting to the thinking of this world will always result in fear. However, when our minds are renewed in God, we're able to see and think clearly. God doesn't want us to be afraid. The spirit of self-control comes to us as we renew our minds.

What does renewing your mind look like day by day? How does seeking the Lord replace fear with self-control?

Why is looking to the Lord to receive a spirit of self-control better than willing ourselves to be self-controlled?

God has given us the spirit of a sound mind, but we need to engage it and inform it with truths from God's Word. This is why, before responding to circumstances or relationships, we ought to form the habit of pausing and asking ourselves, *Am I in my right mind? Am I seeking to think according to God's thoughts, or am I thinking on my own?* When our minds are transformed and renewed, our thinking follows the truths of Scripture and the guidance of the Holy Spirit.

What difference do you think the previous questions would make in the way you respond to circumstances and relationships?

Unreliable thinking comes to us without being invited. Ideas pop into our heads whose origins are highly questionable. James wrote:

Let no one say when he is tempted, "I am being tempted by God,"
for God cannot be tempted with evil, and he himself tempts no one.
But each person is tempted when he is lured and enticed by his own
desire. Then desire when it has conceived gives birth to sin, and sin
when it is fully grown brings forth death.
JAMES 1:13-15

Before those ideas ever come to us, we need to work with God's Spirit to renew our minds so that we can respond from God's nature instead of our own. Fearful thinking comes from a spirit of fear, and we must reject it with power, love, and a sound mind. Believers must fight day by day, moment by moment to press the truths of God deep into our hearts and minds.

What does the process of depending on God's Word look like for you? When do you take time to study God's Word? To pray? To meditate on Scripture?

If you've never made these disciplines regular practices in your life, who could help you develop them?

If you already practice these disciplines regularly, what difference do you notice in your thinking when you've devoted time to the Scriptures versus when you haven't?

Write 2 Timothy 1:7 on a card; post it over your bathroom sink, on your dashboard, on your refrigerator, or beside your computer; and say it aloud every day for a week. You should then have it memorized. Once you've memorized it, you can pray it: "God, I acknowledge that You haven't given me a spirit of fear but of power, love, and a sound mind. Thank You." As you meditate on this verse, practice responding to circumstances and relationships from a right mind.

As you end this lesson, ask God to show you ways you could let His Word more consistently guide your thinking. Then quietly sit before Him and record any ideas He brings to mind.

DAY 5
LIVING BEYOND FEAR

Fear is really one of God's gifts. Its function is to arouse our attention to the fact that something is happening that we need to respond to: "Take care of yourself!" But as we've seen this week, the problem is that we develop unhealthy and immobilizing fears; we get stuck. When fear is irrational, we call it a phobia. When it's mild but persistent, we call it an aversion. When it's persistent and overwhelming, we call it dread. When it's immediate and life-threatening, we call it terror. But if fear is induced by an actual threat, it's good. And it's from God.

> **Take a moment to pray and thank God for healthy fear. Ask Him for ongoing grace and wisdom to handle fears the way He wants, employing a spirit of power, love, and a sound mind to do this.[1]**

The best use of the ability to fear is to learn to fear God. To understand the fear of God, let's use a different definition of *fear* today:

> **Fear:** *the attitude of heart that seeks a right relationship to its source*

> **Read Luke 23:32-43. Three men were facing the agonizing death of crucifixion. Where and when is the fear of God mentioned in this passage? What point is being made?**

Previously this week we've focused on what we shouldn't fear. Today we'll think about what or whom we should fear. When God gets a grip on our lives, we feel something. In Scripture every time someone had a genuine encounter with God, the person was on his or her face before Him. When God shows us a fraction of His glory, our response is fear—a humble, holy reverence of Him. It's as if a veil drops from our eyes and we gasp at how great and how close and how real He is. God's glory overwhelms us. When we also sense in that instant how unlike us He is in His holiness, power, sovereignty, and attributes, fear is clearly the appropriate response. Then He graciously releases us from that instinctive posture. In Scripture God and His messengers are always quick to say, "Fear not!"

In those moments we desperately want to be in a right relationship with God. Don't allow a particular sin to persist in your life for days, weeks, or months. Salvation may have taken the fear of hell away, but never let it take away your holy fear of being in true connection with the living God through His Son, Jesus Christ.

What are some instances in your life when you've experienced the fear of the Lord?

Probably the clearest indication that God has gripped your heart is a heightened reverence and respect for His Word. How much power does God's Word have over your life? Can God's Word change your opinion on a subject? Are you through treating God's Word like a salad bar—a little of that, some of this, and none of that? God says:

This is the one to whom I will look:
he who is humble and contrite in spirit
and trembles at my word.
ISAIAH 66:2

How do you respond to the statements you just read? In what ways do they describe your experiences with God?

The people in the Bible show us an amazing, healthy transparency before God when it comes to the matter of fears. Notice these two declarations David made in the same psalm:

When I am afraid,
I put my trust in you.
PSALM 56:3

In God I trust; I shall not be afraid.
What can man do to me?
PSALM 56:11

So what's it going to be, David? Are you afraid or not afraid? The psalmist lets us see that it's both. Fears happen, and when they do, we engage a spirit of right thinking and trust the Lord. And the more we trust the Lord, the more we discover that the things we fear are less and less likely to provoke us to act afraid.

What replaces fear? Internally, faith; externally, boldness, courage, and action. Even when we act with boldness, fear can still be present as an emotional response, but it doesn't get the final vote on our decisions. We choose to act in the presence of fear because some things are more important than fear and because we know someone who's greater than any fear we might experience.

Take Peter, for example. Out of fear he denied Jesus three times. But later in Acts 4 Peter testified of Jesus with boldness. The word translated "boldness" (see vv. 13, 29,31) could also be translated as "courage" or "confidence." So what changed for Peter? First, Jesus restored their fellowship (see John 21:15-19). Second, Peter was filled with the Holy Spirit (see Acts 2). The love of Jesus and the power of the Spirit gave Peter a spirit of self-control, love, and power. His experience with God led to a life marked by boldness.

When have you experienced supernatural boldness that can come only from God? In what areas of your life do you need such boldness?

Spend a moment meditating on this week's memory verse:

God gave us a spirit not of fear but of power and love and self-control.
2 TIMOTHY 1:7

Spend time in prayer committing to practice what God has taught you about getting unstuck from fear. Thank Him for giving you a spirit of power, love, and a sound mind.

1. For more on right-mindedness and self-control, see Pastor James's Bible study *Think Differently* (LifeWay, 2016).

WEEK 6
GETTING UNSTUCK FROM NEGATIVITY

Welcome to session 6 of Unstuck.

Begin with a short prayer thanking God for the lessons of the past five weeks. Because this is the final group session, members may want to take a few minutes to share experiences of traction they've gained. This might also be a good time to plan or promote what the group will study next.

Use some or all of the following questions to prepare the group for the video teaching.

What do you find easiest to complain about?

Would you admit to struggling with negativity? Why is negativity such a common struggle?

As a general rule, most people err toward the negative or the positive. However, once negativity is introduced into a conversation or a relationship, getting unstuck from this trap can be difficult. Negativity has an inherent toxicity that spreads quickly.

Why is it so easy to continue being negative when we head down that path?

As we begin the session, we admit that for many of us, negativity is a common struggle. Most of us wish negativity were a less frequent or rare struggle in our lives. In the video teaching, Pastor James will examine the way God deals with negativity in His people.

WATCH

Use this guide to follow along as you watch video session 6.

Negativity is sin.

Complaining

To express dissatisfaction with a circumstance that is not wrong and about which I am doing nothing myself to correct

Criticism

To dwell on the perceived faults of another with no view or action for their good

Negativity

Faithless, loveless, destructive words about people or situations that only ventilate my flesh

God hears our negativity.

Negativity distorts reality.

Five Logs on the Negativity Fire

1. A critical eye

2. Wrong expectations

3. Negative friends

4. Unresolved hurt

5. Bad time management

God hears our negativity; therefore, own it.

God hates our negativity.

My negativity + God's hearing = God's anger.

The Spirit of grace is God giving you forgiveness because of what Jesus Christ did.

God judges our negativity.

Video sessions available at lifeway.com/unstuck or with a subscription to smallgroup.com

Discuss the video teaching with your group.

Why is negativity sin?

Pastor James said complaining is "to express dissatisfaction with a circumstance that isn't wrong and that I'm doing nothing myself to correct." What are the three parts of this definition? Why is each significant?

Respond to this definition of *criticism:* **"to dwell on the perceived faults of another with no view toward or action for their good." What makes criticism unconstructive?**

How does negativity destroy the effectiveness of the spirit of love, power, and self-control that we studied last week?

What are the five logs on the negativity fire? In your experience, which negativity log causes the fires of conflict to burn hottest?

What advice did Pastor James give to combat negativity in ourselves? Which teaching do you need to tell yourself more often? Why?

When you want to respond to a situation with negativity, how could you respond differently?

APPLICATION: Because this is the final group session, let's take a few minutes to wait quietly before the Lord and ask Him to make clear to us any guidance from His Word over the past six weeks that can free us from being stuck. Take this opportunity to confess to one another and depend on one another for prayer. After time for sharing, close with prayer.

THIS WEEK'S MEMORY VERSE

These things took place as examples for us, that we might not desire evil as they did.
1 CORINTHIANS 10:6

ASSIGNMENT. Complete the daily lessons this week to conclude this study. Pray for each member of your group by name, asking the Holy Spirit to continue His good work of getting their lives unstuck.

SLIPPERY ROAD AHEAD

So far in this study we've looked at the process of gaining traction in the common struggles of depression, marriage, sexual sins, and fear. If we've struggled with one or more of those issues, we may feel negative about the prospects of gaining traction. And if we can't personally identify with any of those struggles, we might be critical and complain about people who are stuck in those problems. Negativity attacks us one way or another.

That's why we need to understand negativity, be able to spot the telltale signs that it's operating, and make sure we see it from God's perspective. We learned early in this study that any struggle or problem won't be resolved until it's recognized. We won't do anything to gain traction until we're fully convinced that we're stuck.

If you're not sure whether negativity is a problem for you, consider asking someone who's close enough to you to be gut-level honest. Ask them whether you're a negative person. If so, ask them when and about what you seem to be most negative. The answers may surprise you. All of us are likely negative about some things. When we identify not only the presence of negativity but also the specific circumstances that produce this quality in our lives, we'll be better equipped to deal with it.

Negativity is an important issue because it affects our witness. Christians should be joyful people, but negativity obscures a joyful spirit. To be salt and light in the world, as Jesus called us to be in Matthew 5:13-16, we must put negativity aside.

If we're not stuck in negativity, someone close to us probably is and may be ready to accept our help. We've learned over the past five weeks that not only is God willing and ready to help those who are stuck, but He also provides us with brothers and sisters in Christ who can give us hands-on help to gain or maintain traction in the slippery places of life.

DAY 1
NEGATIVITY IS SIN

For our final week of study, we'll look at the common struggle of negativity, highlighting two of its most destructive components: complaining and criticism. We complain about circumstances, and we criticize people. Here are definitions of the terms that describe our struggle.

Complaining: *to express dissatisfaction with a circumstance that isn't wrong and that I'm doing nothing myself to correct*

Criticism: *to dwell on the perceived faults of another with no view toward or action for their good*

Negativity: *faithless, loveless, destructive words about people or situations that only ventilate my flesh and don't advance God's purposes*

Why do you think we're bent toward negativity? In what ways are we prone to excuse or overlook our tendencies to complain and criticize?

Read Numbers 11:1-6; 12:1-2. What were the general and specific complaints of the people of Israel? What did Aaron and Miriam criticize Moses about?

Review the previous definitions. What was particularly destructive about both of these instances? Who was the audience for this negativity?

Why did God view both of these behaviors as sin?

Whether or not we realize it, negativity—in both its complaining and critical forms—is always expressed to two audiences: a horizontal one and a vertical one. Other people (horizontal) and God (vertical) witness our negativity. When complaining is in our head, it's not a problem; when complaining is in our mouths and in our ears, it's a problem. You can't keep critical thoughts from coming into your head. But when you express them in words and actions, you're sliding into a rut.

Internally, what can we do with complaints and critical thoughts while rejecting the option of expressing them?

The wisdom of last week's memory verse can be applied to the problem of negativity. Second Timothy 1:7 assures us that God has given us a spirit of power for circumstances, love for relationships, and a sound mind for internal struggles.

What's an example of applying power to a circumstance instead of complaining about it?

What's an example of loving someone instead of criticizing him or her?

How does a sound mind help us win the internal battle against verbalizing complaints and criticism of others?

Read 1 Corinthians 10:1-13.

The context makes it clear that when Paul wrote "these things" in verses 6 and 11, he had in mind the events recorded in Numbers.

When the people complained about their circumstances and Aaron and Miriam criticized Moses, in what ways did those actions express a desire for evil, according to 1 Corinthians 10:6?

Negativity that's expressed as complaints or criticism is sin. In fact, the definition we're using makes this point in multiple ways. *Negativity* is "faithless, loveless, destructive words about people and situations that only ventilate my flesh and don't advance God's purposes."

In what ways is negativity sin by that definition? Identify at least five.

The more we make negativity the default setting of our attitudes, the more we ignore the historical example God recorded and preserved to help us. Negativity increasingly becomes a low estimation of everything but our own thoughts. As it did with the Israelites' complaints, our negativity distorts our perception of reality. They complained as if they'd lived in the palace of Pharaoh and enjoyed the abundant produce of Egypt instead of being miserable slaves.

How have you seen negativity distort reality in your life?

The key to understanding the damaging nature of negativity is found in the final phrase of each definition we're using for *complaining* ("that isn't wrong and that I'm doing nothing myself to correct") and for *criticism* ("with no view toward or action for their good"). Expressing dissatisfaction or disagreement when something is wrong isn't complaining; it's confronting evil. Seeking permission to lovingly, gently, and humbly point out a fault isn't criticism; it's practicing tough love. In contrast, complaining and criticism have no such redemptive ends in mind.

Spend a moment meditating on this week's memory verse:

These things took place as examples for us, that we might not desire evil as they did.
1 CORINTHIANS 10:6

Spend a few moments reviewing your attitudes over the past week. Where did negativity spring up? Do you need to repent of any negativity?

As you end this lesson, ask God to make this week a clear step in a new direction away from negativity for you and the rest of your group.

DAY 2
GOD SEES OUR NEGATIVITY

Yesterday we focused on the relational damage that negativity does at a human level. Now we're going to take it to the ultimate level. God is the all-seeing, all-hearing audience to our complaining and criticism. God's Word demonstrates just how seriously He takes all He sees and hears.

Read Hebrews 4:12-13. In what ways does the surgical precision of God's Word affect particular areas of our lives?

Which areas of our lives are we most aware of when God's truth is operating on them?

The terms verse 12 uses to describe the parts of us that God's Word penetrates aren't intended as specific or technical descriptions of our makeup. They're used to indicate that no area of our lives can escape the incisive truth of God's Word. It cuts between truth and falsehood, pretense and reality. Of special interest for our study is Scripture's uncanny way of "discerning the thoughts and intentions of the heart" (v. 12). We may rationalize our motives and actions, but God's Word cuts to the truth.

Read Numbers 11:1; 12:1-2. What drove the people to complain and criticize?

God is aware of our wholehearted worship, half-hearted praise, and hidden complaints. He knows that when we complain about situations and criticize others, we're indirectly complaining about and criticizing Him. These two incidents happened shortly after the people of Israel left Mount Sinai. God had miraculously and fantastically delivered His people from their slavery and oppression. Yet they complained about their misfortunes.

At any moment in your experiences, have conditions ever been such that you said, "God is allowing more evil than good into my life"? Why?

How did that situation end, and what did you learn about God from it?

Instead of experiencing the sweet-smelling aroma of gratitude, love, and obedience rising from us, God is assaulted with our demands, as if we were the ones in charge, as if we were the center of the universe. One reason the story of Job is included in Scripture is to painfully clarify that the world doesn't revolve around us and that God doesn't have to answer to us. One of Job's discoveries in particular ought to inform our thinking when we're tempted to complain and criticize.

Read Job 42:1-6. When we're stuck in complaining and criticism, what does Job identify as the starting point for gaining traction?

Today and tomorrow we'll look at five logs we throw into the flames of negativity, which stoke them until they're all-consuming. Here are the first two.

1. A CRITICAL EYE. Do problems, flaws, and mistakes naturally jump out at you everywhere you look, or do you tend to overlook what you consider minor issues and focus on the rosy big picture? Neither perspective is perfect, but the critical eye can cause far more damage through destructive comments, although it can also lead to good by pointing out actual problems.

What's the difference between unhealthy, negative criticism and constructive, meaningful criticism?

What does a constantly critical heart reveal about our relationship with God?

2. UNEXAMINED EXPECTATIONS. Assumptions and anticipation are unavoidable parts of life, but we have to evaluate them by standards outside ourselves, primarily God's Word. We often have wrong expectations based on self-centeredness and sin. A common expectation involves the changes in other people we want or don't want to see. However, that work must be done by God and them. A negative response on our part can indicate that we were expecting certain results we had no right to expect. God may never change some situations and people.

One key question to ask ourselves when examining expectations is, *In this situation or with this person, do I expect my will or God's will to be done?* The answer will indicate the nature of our expectations.

> **Do you think any difficulties or disappointments in your relationships and situations might indicate that you hold wrong expectations? What signs are evident?**

> **What would it take for you to release those people, relationships, and circumstances to God's will and stop expecting your will to be done?**

> **Spend a moment meditating on this week's memory verse:**

> *These things took place as examples for us, that we might not desire evil as they did.*
> **1 CORINTHIANS 10:6**

> **How are the negative examples of Scripture meant to draw us away from negativity?**

> **Tomorrow we'll look at three more logs we often add to the flames of our negativity. For now, make the matters of a critical eye and wrong expectations a focus of prayer as you end today's lesson.**

DAY 3
A BONFIRE OF NEGATIVITY

God hears and sees us. Scripture says there's no filter between God and us:

> *No creature is hidden from his sight, but all are naked and exposed to the eyes of him to whom we must give account.*
> **HEBREWS 4:13**

The less we cultivate an awareness of God's oversight and presence in our lives, the more likely we are to embrace negativity. And the less likely we are to be humbled and serious about the account we'll eventually give to Him.

If God brought before you all the negativity, complaining, and criticism from the past few months, what would be the tone of that report? Overall, how are you doing in regard to negativity?

Yesterday we looked at two highly combustible items we throw into the fire of negativity to make it burn hotter. Today we'll add three more.

3. NEGATIVE FRIENDS. Genuine Christian friendships guard against negativity because those relationships urge us toward Christlikeness. But if we choose certain kinds of friends, we'll find company around the bonfire of negativity.

For example, if you surround yourself with wrongdoers, wrongdoing comes easily. If your friends aren't friends of faith, they'll draw you in a negative direction. If your friends are prone to doubt, when you've finished a phone conversation with them, you'll regret that you took their call. Every time you listen, you get an earful of what's wrong with the world, what's wrong with their life, what's wrong with your hair, and what's wrong with everything else. Reduce the negativity in your life by graciously breaking with these friends. Life is too short. Family is forever; friends are optional. It's crucial to surround yourself with positive, Christ-oriented friends.

What friendships might be fostering an overly negative attitude in your life? Are they or you the primary source of that negativity?

What gracious step do you need to take to break off a certain negative relationship?

4. UNRESOLVED HURT. Negativity often flows from unhealed wounds and unsettled conflict. These issues must be resolved. When you haven't acknowledged pain or identified its source, it wells up inside you and comes out elsewhere. Thank God for patient, loving spouses and friends who've absorbed your misplaced negativity, but don't keep passing on hurt to others. Let it go. Move on.

When you identify an unresolved hurt, what steps do you take to heal or settle it?

5. POOR TIME MANAGEMENT. A schedule that's out of control leads to a lot of negativity. If you have too much time on your hands, you're just a computer screen and a mouse away from becoming an Internet troll, searching for significance and leaving cynical comments everywhere just trying to be heard. No one is blessed by that. You're not helping anybody if you have too much time on your hands.

If you have too little time on your hands and you're late for everything or rushing all the time, you have a time-management problem. You'll become negative in a hurry and express your frustration by blaming or burdening other people because you've taken on too much. It's better to do far fewer things than to get stuck in this rut of negativity.

Don't use your time poorly and let negativity be the result. Whether you have too much time or not enough, it can be a log on the negativity fire because your time management is out of control.

Which of these five logs are contributing to negativity in your life?

We should be grieved to know that God hears our negativity. The truth is, He puts up with negativity to a point. Tomorrow we'll look at the time when Israel reached that point with God. Let's learn from that example so that we don't test it personally. It's better to enjoy God, who longs to be for us.

Read Exodus 34:6-9. In what ways have you experienced the truth of this self-description by God?

How would imitating Moses' response in verses vv. 8-9 help you put out the fire of negativity in your life?

Spend a moment meditating on this week's memory verse:

These things took place as examples for us, that we might not desire evil as they did.
1 CORINTHIANS 10:6

What are you desiring from God as you seek to get unstuck from negativity?

As you end today's lesson, pray for wisdom to be more aware of God's oversight of and attentiveness to your thoughts and words each day.

DAY 4
HOW GOD FEELS ABOUT OUR NEGATIVITY

God hates our negativity. He hears it, sees what it does to us, and hates it. And at a certain point He does something about it.

Read Numbers 11:1-3; 12:9. How did God feel about the negativity that the Israelites exhibited in these two instances?

Don't miss the cause-effect formula revealed in these passages:

My negativity + God's hearing = God's anger.

You can do the math. Each part of the equation leads to the next. Our negativity is our sin-infused response to events and people around us, deeply rooted in us. The expression of our negativity has an audience made up of other people and always God, who hears not only what comes from our mouths but also what's in our hearts and minds that goes unsaid. The rest of our audience may agree or disagree with our attitude, based on their limited external evidence, but God sees the whole picture:

The Lord sees not as man sees: man looks on the outward appearance, but the Lord looks on the heart.
1 SAMUEL 16:7

When God responded to the Israelites in the wilderness, He did so with anger. And He can do so with us.

What does God do when He sees something in you that makes Him angry?

When Christians discuss this equation, their comments are predictable: "My, my, Pastor James! Don't you know that all of God's anger for our sin was poured out on Jesus on the cross? God isn't angry with us. We're saved; we're forgiven; we're loved. Pastor, you need to get out of the Old Testament!"

The facts in that statement are all true, but the conclusions may be questionable. All of God's anger for our sin was poured out on Jesus on the cross. And if you've turned from your sin and embraced Jesus Christ, you're saved, forgiven, and loved. But the persistent presence of negativity in a believer's life, like any sin, must be dealt with. And God has a plan to deal with that negativity:

> *If we go on sinning deliberately after receiving the knowledge of the truth, there no longer remains a sacrifice for sins, but a fearful expectation of judgment, and a fury of fire that will consume the adversaries. Anyone who has set aside the law of Moses dies without mercy on the evidence of two or three witnesses. How much worse punishment, do you think, will be deserved by the one who has trampled underfoot the Son of God, and has profaned the blood of the covenant by which he was sanctified, and has outraged the Spirit of grace?*
> **HEBREWS 10:26-29**

"If we go on sinning deliberately" (v. 26) expresses a warning against a certain attitude that says, "I know what the gospel says, and I'm forgiven. I can continue sinning for as long as I want." On the contrary, the truth and grace of the gospel have to take root in our lives and bear fruit.

You can debate with me about whether God is angry, but I can tell you this for a fact: if you don't think humbling yourself under the Word of God and living to please the God who saved you is your primary mission in life, then you're not saved.

We can't use the cross as an excuse for continual sin rather than a continual reminder of how much God loves us. The Lord has strong feelings about negativity, and saved people care about what God says about what He hears.

What do you do when you discover that you've been unintentionally or deliberately doing something God hates and calls sin?

God hates how destructive negativity is to us and to others. The time and energy we waste are staggering. And we immeasurably harm others when we claim to trust God and be His people while behaving as if we can't trust Him and as if being His people makes no difference in the way we live. The people of Israel walking out of the shadow of Mount Sinai were supposed to be living representatives to the nations of a God worth worshiping and obeying. We who bear the name of Christ have no less of a task before us.

Why is negativity not only sin against God but also unloving to others?

Do you think about your seemingly minor sins as offenses that God hates? If not, why not?

Love has no room for complaining or criticism. Others are desperate to see real love in action, and Jesus told us our relationships with one another are a testimony to the world:

By this all people will know that you are my disciples, if you have love for one another.
JOHN 13:35

In what areas of your current circumstances or relationships can you ask God to help you replace negativity with love?

Spend a moment meditating on this week's memory verse:

These things took place as examples for us, that we might not desire evil as they did.
1 CORINTHIANS 10:6

As you end today's lesson, ask God to give you ears to hear when expressions of negativity invade your conversations, as well as wisdom to keep quiet.

DAY 5
WHAT GOD DOES WITH NEGATIVITY

In the case of the Israelites' negativity, God fought fire with fire. The people had already established a rebellious, ungrateful attitude almost immediately after leaving Egypt, and God was no longer willing to let those flames of negativity go unchecked. He started an actual fire of His own that began to consume the camp. He judged the Israelites' sin.

> **Read Numbers 11:1-3; 12:1-11. What forms did God's judgment take in these two cases?**

> **How long had the Lord suffered the complaining of the Hebrews? What does that teach us about God's grace even in our disobedience?**

The Israelites' negativity fire was burning rampant in the heart of the camp, and God's fire began to consume tents and people on the edges. The people, so distant from God, didn't cry out to Him but to Moses. His prayer stopped the fire, but it didn't stop the rumble of complaining. The negativity resumed in 11:4. In fact, the undercurrent would continue until they arrived for the first time at the border of the promised land and the people balked in fear and faithlessness.

In Aaron and Miriam's case, sibling rivalry took the form of criticism of Moses' wife. Their problem was Zipporah's race, which didn't matter to God. But their underlying complaint was about the unfairness they perceived when God recognized Moses as His primary spokesman rather than all three of them. God wasn't going to allow this petty rift to break up the team that was leading the people, so He forcefully moved to stop the criticism (see 12:9-10).

God hears our negativity, so we need to own it. God hates it, so we need to stop it. Because if we don't, God judges it. The results are pretty hard to miss in the passages you read in Numbers 11–12. God brought sudden, painful consequences to bear on the perpetrators. Choose to sin; choose to suffer.

In persistent sinful behavior we cross a line that only God knows and that determines when judgment will fall. Our biggest mistake is assuming there's no line to cross or no willingness on God's part to bring about judgment. We fail to recognize that God's love joins His holiness in bringing judgment. God's patience isn't nullified by judgment; it's simply applied in a way that pushes us toward repentance. And "slow to anger" (Ex. 34:6) doesn't mean "incapable of getting angry," particularly when anger is the required response.

Read Hebrews 12:4-11. What reasons does this passage give for God's discipline?

According to these verses, what should our response be when discipline comes?

This week we've looked at two incidents that happened in the wilderness of Sinai many centuries ago. It's tempting to avoid the immediate lesson of these verses by saying, "Man! That happened a long time ago!" But notice a verse that's very similar to 1 Corinthians 10:6, this week's memory verse:

These things happened to them as an example, but they were written down for our instruction, on whom the end of the ages has come.
1 CORINTHIANS 10:11

We can't say we didn't get a warning. This verse even adds the point that God had these examples recorded so that they could teach us over and over. As long as God's written Word stands, it will include these lessons for followers of Jesus.

Think about the losses of traction we've addressed in this Bible study: depression, marriage, sexual sin, fear, and negativity. Which topic has had the biggest impact on your way of thinking?

Which area includes unfinished business you need to revisit?

Any Bible study can bring internal conflict and the painful realization that repentance is necessary. As we've said throughout this study, you can't gain traction until you admit you're stuck. When you reach that point of surrender, you can have hope and a good reason to worship because you know God won't abandon you when you're stuck.

Even if you're experiencing God's discipline in a rut of your own making, you can have joy in the middle of your tears by applying Hebrews 12:4-11 . And you'll find hope in Hebrews 12:1-3 by realizing that your struggles are common and that other believers are cheering you on, encouraging you from the bleachers of history or even in your small group. The words "Let us also lay aside every weight, and sin which clings so closely, and let us run with endurance the race that is set before us" (v. 1) are vivid pictures of traction and staying unstuck. Then verse 2 reminds you to keep your eyes on Jesus, the only One who can provide orientation and equilibrium when you start to slide and lose traction:

> ... *looking to Jesus, the founder and perfecter of our faith, who for the joy that was set before him endured the cross, despising the shame, and is seated at the right hand of the throne of God.*
> **HEBREWS 12:2**

If you have sins you'd like to repent of, spend a few minutes in prayer. Invite God to continue His good work in you. Spend time in silence so that He can impress on you His love, direction, and encouragement to keep following His Son. Arrange to talk to another brother or sister in Christ in the next few days, confessing your struggles to them and sharing what you've learned about the freedom of traction. Be ready to encourage them in their common struggles.

As you end your study, meditate on this week's memory verse:

> *These things took place as examples for us, that we might not desire evil as they did.*
> **1 CORINTHIANS 10:6**

STUDY START DATE

_____ / _____ / _____

Record a few details about this season of your life.

FAMILY |

_____   _____
name   age

_____   _____

_____

_____   _____

_____   _____

WORK |

_____
company

_____
position

HOME |

_____   _____
city   state

What do you hope to get out of this study?

hot

Mark your spiritual temperature.

cold

MAJOR EVENTS IN THE WORLD |

_____

_____

KEY ISSUES IN YOUR WORLD |

_____

_____

Also from
JAMES MACDONALD

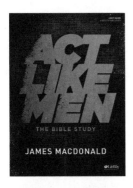

ACT LIKE MEN
The Bible Study
6 sessions

Walk through the five pillars of 1 Corinthians 16:13-14 to encourage and challenge yourself in becoming a stronger man of God.

Leader Kit 005399892
Bible Study Book 005802240

LORD, CHANGE MY ATTITUDE
Before It's Too Late
10 sessions

Reject attitudes God hates—like complaining, coveting, criticizing—and replace them with those He honors—thankfulness, contentment, love, and more.

Leader Kit 005790074
Bible Study Book 005790073

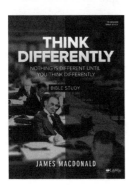

THINK DIFFERENTLY
Nothing Is Different Until You Think Differently
10 sessions

Learn to renew your mind in Christ as you identify and overcome the mental, familial, and even self-created strongholds that enslave you.

Leader Kit 005399896
Bible Study Book 005644087

STUDY END DATE

_____ / _____ / _____

★ **TOP FIVE FAVORITE POINTS FROM THIS STUDY**

page #

_____

_____

_____

_____

_____

**WHERE DID
YOU STUDY?**

**WITH WHOM DID YOU
DO THIS STUDY?**

○ **Home**

○ **Church**

○ **Another home:**
_____

○ **Other:**
_____

_____

_____

_____

_____

**WITH WHOM DO
YOU WANT TO SHARE
THIS STUDY?**

_____

BIBLE VERSES TO MEMORIZE